THE FARMER'S GUIDE TO THE LAW

THE FARMER'S GUIDE
TO THE LAW

by

D. H. CHAPMAN
A.R.I.C.S., Q.A.L.A.S., F.A.I.
Head of the Department of Rural Studies, College of Estate Management

and

J. V. DAVIES
LL.B., of Gray's Inn, Barrister-at-Law
Legal Secretary to the National Farmers' Union

Illustrated by GUS of the 'Evening News'

1962

THE ESTATES GAZETTE LIMITED
28 DENMARK STREET · LONDON · WC2

PRINTED IN GREAT BRITAIN BY
WALKER & CO. (PRINTERS) LTD.
162 COLNE ROAD, TWICKENHAM, MIDDX.

PREFACE

We ask you to look on this book as a guide through the tangled legal undergrowth which surrounds British farming in the nineteen-sixties. We detest expressions like "agribusiness" or "vertical integration", but we cannot escape the events which have brought them into being. Farming for profit has always been a matter calling for wise buying and selling, but the rapid changes which have in recent years transformed the industries from which the farmer buys as well as those into which his produce is sold for grinding, canning, bottling, processing or packing, have brought him into a tough and competitive commercial world in which he must be forever signing complex agreements.

Nor is his trading the only aspect of a farmer's life which forces him to think of his legal rights and responsibilities. As a landowner or occupier, he may have to face fierce competition from local authorities or others for the very land which forms his solid raw material. As an employer he must tread delicately through a network of rules and regulations which govern the wages, insurance, housing and safety of his workpeople. As a tax-payer he must . . . well, farming isn't solely a question of greenfingery!

We do not think that farmers are specially prone to law suits. On the contrary those whose work is so bound up with unhurried processes of nature might be expected to be extremely cautious in their affairs. In the courts they have had some notable successes, and, inevitably, some expensive failures. But country solicitors do not get extraordinarily fat. This book is intended neither to glorify nor detract from their work. We have tried to deal in comprehensive form with many of the problems with which rural lawyers, valuers, land agents and others must be familiar in the lives of their clients, and for that reason it may be that some of them will want to have this book on their shelves. If so, then we hope we may be found to have avoided undue distortion in reducing our material to manageable size.

But this is not in any sense a lawyer's book. It is intended to bring to the farmer's own desk a closer appreciation of the legal aspects of quite ordinary events and relationships. Today he may be taking on a new stockman; tomorrow he may have to see the landlord's agent upon a rather delicate matter; on Wednesday night there's a meeting to talk about setting up a co-operative machinery syndicate; on Thursday a friendly visit from the District Valuer to settle the compensation for the easement for the new water main; and did he know he might have to pay rates on that broiler-house ? These are common enough happenings in the farmer's or commercial grower's calendar. Perhaps this book, by providing a middle course between taking professional advice, and taking no advice at all, may help him to avoid some of the commoner traps which the law sets for everyone.

D.H.C.

The College of Estate Management,
Kensington, W.8

J.V.D.

Agriculture House,
Knightsbridge, S.W.1

CONTENTS

CONTENTS

INTRODUCTION

THE FARMER'S GUIDE TO THE LAW

Any book of non-fiction must inevitably make use of terms and conventions unfamiliar to some of its readers. Ours is no exception; hence these few explanatory words to the reader unlearned in law.

How law comes about

Our law derives from several sources. The earliest is known as the *common law*, whose origins cannot be dated: it arose from the ordinary habit of making up the rules as the game proceeds. The conservative approach of the King's judges led to a general acceptance of past decisions and time-honoured procedures, while the gradual growth of law reporting—lawyers' records of the facts, arguments and decisions in important cases—from the 13th century onwards, reduced to writing the vast body of judge-made law, the common law. A typical common law rule is that which places a duty on a farmer to fence his cattle so that they do not stray on to his neighbour's land and cause damage.

By comparison, *statute law* is, as it were, made to measure, and continually emerging from our parliamentary machine. It mainly takes the form of Acts of Parliament, supplemented by Statutory Instruments. The latter entail much less of the paraphernalia attending the conception and birth of an Act. They are made, with the authority of Parliament and under the powers strictly laid down in the enabling Act, by the appropriate Minister of the Crown, e.g., the Minister of Agriculture, Fisheries and Food.

A third source of law fills the unforeseen holes in the pattern of statute law. For example, the Local Government Act, 1929, did away with the payment of local rates on agricultural land and buildings. The Act may appear to define comprehensively " agricultural land and buildings "; but what about temporary caravan sites and land used for turf-cutting, are they sufficiently agricultural to escape local rates? Such questions frequently rest with the courts, where it falls to the judges to act as interpreters.

The Courts

Because we shall have to refer, for instance, to the Magistrates' Court or the Court of Appeal, it may help the reader if we list the various courts and show to what extent the decisions of each constitute " precedents " binding on the others. We might almost explain this by means of a diagram, which would be roughly pyramid-shaped, with the House of Lords at the top. But in deference to the humble and impecunious litigant we begin—with him—in the so-called " inferior courts ", where justice is tempered with economy.

Inferior Courts. These include the County Courts (which hear civil cases only, i.e., those between persons), Quarter Sessions (criminal cases, i.e., those in which the State plays a part), and Magistrates' Courts (civil and criminal). The decisions they make are binding upon the parties only. They bind no other court— nor even themselves, when next confronted with a case involving similar principles. At most, their decisions will be treated as " persuasive " by their equals or by higher courts in the absence of direct authority from some binding source.

High Court. Her Majesty's Judges and Commissioners of Assize, the Lords Justices of Appeal, the Lord Chief Justice and the Lords of Appeal (the " law lords " of the House of Lords) are all judges of the High Court. In general their decisions are binding upon the lower courts and even upon their equal brethren until reversed or " not followed " by the Court of Appeal or the House of Lords, as the case may be.

Divisions of the High Court. There are three such divisions: Queen's Bench, Chancery, and Probate, Divorce and Admiralty. Throughout the Divisions the decisions of any High Court Judge are binding upon his colleagues, if sitting alone. In turn each is bound by the decisions of the Court of Appeal, civil or criminal as the case may be.

Court of Appeal. This deals with civil cases only. It is bound by the decisions of the House of Lords and by its own decisions.

Court of Criminal Appeal. This is the equivalent of the last where criminal cases are concerned. It is bound by the House of Lords and itself.

House of Lords. In its judicial, as opposed to its law-making, capacity this is the highest appeal court in the kingdom. It deals with both civil and criminal appeals, and its decisions are binding on all courts, including itself. They can be over-ruled only by Act of Parliament.

PART 1

MAINLY FOR TENANT FARMERS

On taking possession of somebody else's land, the farmer walks into the web of a body of law known as Landlord and Tenant. This tells him what he may and must do with the farm and the farming, and puts him and his landlord under many obligations towards one another.

In this part of the book we begin with the tenant's agreeing to take the farm, proceed with the privileges and pitfalls that await him during the tenancy, and end with his rights to compensation on quitting and how they are settled.

Chapter 1

TENURE AND RENT

THE AGREEMENT

A tenancy agreement, in the popular sense of the term, is the document the farmer has kept in the third pigeonhole in the roll-top desk undisturbed since he signed the landlord's copy on taking the farm. Sometimes it begins *This Agreement,* sometimes *This Lease,* the distinction between which we may disregard here without leading our readers astray. It consists of a number of "clauses" dealing with such things as the rent and when it is payable; rights to trees, minerals, game; the rotation of crops or the farming system to be followed; responsibility for repairs, and so forth.

The obvious advantage of a well-drawn agreement is that in case of dispute the answer is there in writing. It is a *contract,* therefore not to be gone back upon unless both " parties "— landlord and tenant—agree to its amendment.

However, an agreement to let a farm need not be in writing at all. Very many farms, especially the smaller ones, are let by word of mouth. While in most cases writing is to be preferred, yet once a tenant has legally taken over he cannot be thrown out merely because he has nothing in writing to show how he came to be there. For most of the matters which go into written agreements are covered by Acts of Parliament, and all in all they ensure fair play for both sides. Before tackling separately the more everyday of these matters, two points should be made clear:—

(1) Where an Act of Parliament says one thing and a written agreement another, in some cases the Act takes priority, in others the agreement overrides the Act. This is more easily explained as we go along.

(2) If there is no written agreement, and either the landlord or the tenant would feel happier to have the thing in black and white, he can insist on one being made. This is the procedure, as laid down in section 5 of the Agricultural Holdings Act, 1948.

How to secure a written agreement

To begin with, both the law and common politeness require that whichever party, landlord or tenant, is pressing the matter, he must first make his request to the other party, tenant or land-

lord. If the request is refused, he submits the dispute to arbitration
—a remedy about which more is said in Chapter 6.

The arbitrator's task is to set down in writing the *existing*
unwritten terms of the tenancy; although if both parties are in
agreement they may take this opportunity of altering them. For
instance, the tenant might have been paying his rent once a quarter.
If he would rather in future pay half-yearly, and the landlord
approves, the arbitrator will make that clear in the agreement he
is concocting.

No matter how much else goes in, there are nine matters which
the arbitrator *must* include. The majority may seem no more than
common sense; but then a lot of the law *is* merely common sense
" reduced to writing ". Briefer than the law describes them (in the
First Schedule to the 1948 Act), these are the nine points: —

1. The names of the parties.
2. Description and plan of the farm.
3. The term, or period for which let (see below).
4. The rent and when payable (see p. 4).
5. Who is to pay land tax and rates (see pp. 250 and 276).
6. Responsibility for repairs, etc., (see p. 9).
7. Landlord to insure buildings against fire and, with some
   exceptions, replace them if burnt (see p. 13).
8. Tenant to insure dead stock, hay, straw, etc. (see p. 13).
9. Landlord's right to re-enter the farm if the tenant does not
   carry out his obligations under the agreement (see p. 32).

These are the " musts ". Anything else the arbitrator includes—
for instance, that the landlord shall reserve the right to shoot
pheasants over the farm—is a matter of mutual agreement, not
legal compulsion.

Incidentally, if a written agreement does in fact exist but omits
reference to any one or more of the above matters, either landlord
or tenant can put the same machinery in motion to get the gaps
filled.

Finally, if as a result of altering the liabilities of either party
the arbitrator feels that one of them stands to lose, he may adjust
the rent. For example, if the tenant had been paying £15 a year
in land tax and the landlord agreed to take over the burden from
now on, the arbitrator might excusably say that the rent should
go up by £15 a year to maintain the old balance.

THE TERM

The *length* of time for which a farm is let is called the term, and special rules applying to farms put the tenant-farmer in a much more sitting position than, say, the tenant of a furnished flat.

As a general rule in the landlord and tenant game, if a property is let for a week or for 21 years from today, then in one week or 21 years from now the tenancy automatically ends and the tenant must quit. But if a farm is let for a stated term the general rule does not apply. The tenancy continues, a year at a time, to the end of the world, unless it is *specifically* terminated by either the landlord or the tenant giving not less than one year's notice to quit. " Specifically " means that one of them must do something definite about it; the mere running out (or in legal terms " effluxion ") of time is not sufficient. This provision naturally gives an uncommonly powerful security of tenure to the tenant-farmer who doesn't at all want to leave the old place. His position is further strengthened by the Notice to Quit laws, described in Chapter 4.

Most rules, particularly in law, have their exceptions, and in a very limited number of cases a farm may be let in such a manner than none of the above applies.

One way is to let it for a term less than a year, e.g., " for 364 days from Michaelmas next ". But to do this the parties must get the prior written consent of their County Agricultural Executive Committee (see page 69). If they don't then no matter what any agreement says it becomes a tenancy from year to year, to which all the protection of the law applies.

Again, the land may be let for seasonal grazing or mowing. In many districts it is common to advertise annually: " Sunnybrook Farm. Grazing Rights to be Let by Auction." The successful bidder acquires the right to pasture his cattle on the appropriate portion of Sunnybrook Farm from, say, April to September—but no rights to sow crops, use the milking parlour and so forth. At law this is known as a "licence", not a letting, and it does not need the blessing of the C.A.E.C.

A letting of 18 months

Yet again—and this is one of those knotty points that needed a court case to unravel it—if a farm is let for a betwixt and between period such as 18 months certain, it falls outside the rules we are considering, and the tenant must quit at the end of the term. Although the 1948 Act was drafted so as to bring the maximum number of tenanted farms into its benevolent net, one or two cases are now known to have escaped the parliamentary draftsmen's cunning.

Special care was taken not to allow 364-day agreements to evade the Act by a formula in section 2 converting "interests less than a tenancy from year to year" into yearly tenancies. But in the case of *Gladstone v. Bower*, 1960, it was held that a fixed term of 18 months was an interest *greater* than a tenancy from year to year. Consequently it was not caught by section 2, and the farm tenant was compelled to quit at the end of the 18-month term.

THE RENT

The amount of rent

The amount of rent payable for a farm is in the first instance a matter of bargaining between landlord and tenant, as is the time and manner of payment: half-yearly, quarterly, in advance, in arrear.

If the farm is let for a definite term, say for 21 years, and the lease says that the rent shall be £250 per annum, that figure holds good for those 21 years, unless both landlord and tenant agree to its alteration. But where the tenancy is from year to year either party can get the rent adjusted in the light of changed circumstances.

Ideally, they will talk it over and try to arrange the thing between them. If they cannot, they appoint an arbitrator. The amended section 8 of the 1948 Act gives him his terms of reference, and tells him what he must and must not take into account in assessing the "rent properly payable" for the farm. Fundamentally, the arbitrator must ask himself: "Supposing this farm were let in the open market, with vacant possession, and the landlord and tenant were equally willing to give and take, what rent would it be likely to fetch?" The fact that the tenant, by being actually in occupation, is in a stronger bargaining position must somehow be disregarded. If the tenant has at his own expense increased the rental value by putting up buildings or farming exceptionally well, this too must not be made a reason for raising the rent. On the other hand, if the tenant has been farming badly and so let the farm down, this must not be made an excuse for lowering the rent.

When new rent comes into force

A new rent fixed by an arbitrator comes into effect at the next date on which the tenancy could have been terminated by notice to quit. As we shall see later on, at least one year's notice to quit must be given to terminate the tenancy of the whole or part of a farm, and that notice expires on the appropriate term day. For instance, supposing the term day on a particular farm is Michaelmas, 29th September. The landlord would like to see the rent raised as early as possible. The earliest it can will be a year come Michaelmas next. In order to catch next year's boat, an arbitrator must be appointed at the latest by midnight on 28th September of this year. If the matter is overlooked, and the "date of the reference" (which means the date on which the arbitrator accepts his appointment to act) is delayed until, say, 30th September, then an "arbitrated" rent cannot take effect until the better part of two years from now.

There is a limit to how often the parties can carry their rental wishes to arbitration. An arbitrator-awarded rent cannot take effect sooner than three years since the last time the rent was altered, or sooner than three years from the date the tenancy began.

Increased rent for improvements

Apart from the above provisions, a landlord has rights to an increased rent for a farm where he carries out improvements to it. These improvements must have been done either at the tenant's request or in agreement with him, or under a direction served by the Agricultural Land Tribunal.

Mostly, such improvements fall into the first category. Perhaps the tenant needs a new dutch barn and requests the landlord to provide one. The sensible and usual practice, where the landlord says yes, is for the pair of them to agree, before ever the cement for the floor is ordered, on what extra rent the tenant will pay for it—perhaps 7 or 8 per cent of the cost of supplying and erecting the barn. If, however, the subject is not discussed, or they haven't come to a decision, the landlord may serve a written notice demanding an increased rent within six months of the completion of the job. If the sum cannot be agreed, the matter goes to arbitration. The extra rent that may be charged is " an amount equal to the increase in the rental value of the holding attributable to the carrying out of the improvement ", but where the landlord has received a government grant towards the cost, the increase must be reduced accordingly. The increased rent comes into effect from the date of completion of the improvement.

The same right applies where the A.L.T. direct the landlord to provide certain items of fixed equipment: a matter discussed on page 18.

When rent falls due

A written agreement will invariably state when the rent of a farm becomes due. Usually it is on one of the Quarter Days— Lady Day, Midsummer, Michaelmas, Christmas.* But if a tenancy begins on any " unorthodox " day and the rent is payable quarterly, then quarterly means every three calendar months from the date of commencement.

Rent actually falls due on the morning of the day it is payable, although it is not legally in arrear until midnight. If due on a Sunday it should be paid before midnight on Sunday; there is no holdover until Monday. But if it falls due on a Bank Holiday, it may wait until the day after.

How payment may be enforced

Where a tenant is in arrear with his rent, the landlord has two direct methods of enforcing payment, and one indirect remedy.

The first direct method, known as *recovery by action*, applies where there is a written tenancy agreement containing a clause in which the tenant has agreed in black and white to pay the rent. Here the landlord can bring an action to enforce this promise. In other words, he sues the tenant in the County Court.

The period for which arrears of rent may be recovered is limited to six years. Assuming then that an indulgent or absent-minded landlord allowed his tenant's rent to slide for ten years before taking court action, he would be unable to claim the first four years' arrears. This does not often happen.

Distress

This is the alternative direct method of compelling the payment of overdue rent. It has been described as "the taking, without legal process, of cattle or goods as a pledge to compel the satisfaction of a demand, the performance of a duty, or the redress of an injury." In other words, the landlord or his representative may enter the farm and seize the tenant's goods and chattels to the value of the rent owed.

The law recognises a number of things which may not in any circumstances be distrained upon, ranging from the goods of an

*Since 1752 these have been 25th March, 24th June, 29th September and 25th December respectively; but in many districts the " Old " quarter days linger on, namely 6th April, 6th July, 11th October and 6th January. In fact, over 20 term days are still recognised throughout Britain.

ambassador and his suite to frames, looms and machines used in the woollen, cotton or silk manufactures—which correctly suggests that distress does not apply exclusively to farms. Other things are " conditionally privileged ", that is to say they may be seized only where the landlord cannot find other goods sufficient to cover the rent. They include tools of trade, beasts of the plough and sheep. Nowadays only the most old-fashioned of bailiffs would spare the fattening steers on the grounds that their owner still ploughed with them.

Overriding the general laws of distress, sections 18 to 22 of the 1948 Act bring in many safeguards to ease the defaulting farm tenant's lot. First of all, a landlord may not distrain for rent which became due more than one year before making the distress. This however is extended a bit where, in the ordinary course of dealing between the landlord and the tenant, the payment of rent is deferred a quarter or a half year. For example, on Hungry Gap estate it has long been the practice to hold a rent audit every Midsummer and Christmas. At the first they collect the half-yearly Lady Day rents, at the second the Michaelmas instalment, each a quarter-year after it falls due. Because Farmer Holdback appears to have fallen out of the habit of either appearing or submitting his rent in any other way, distress may be levied on him up to the value of three half-years' arrears.

Then there are special limitations on what may be distrained. Agisted stock—i.e., beasts belonging to another to which the tenant is giving board and lodging—must not be taken if other sufficient distrainable goods are available. If the agisted animals are distrained, the landlord can claim through them only the price their owner agreed to pay for their agistment or any balance not yet paid. And at any time before the landlord sells the animals under the distress proceedings, the owner may redeem them by paying the distrainer the amount of agistment money due.

Agricultural or other machinery hired by the tenant cannot be taken for distress, nor can bulls, stallions, boars, rams and other beasts hired or borrowed from other people for breeding purposes.

Re-entry

The landlord's indirect method of getting satisfaction where a tenant is behind-hand with his rent is open to him only when he has made provision for it in a written agreement by means of a " forfeiture clause ". Since this applies to other breaches of covenant as well as non-payment of rent, it is given a section to itself at page 32.

Chapter 2

FIXED EQUIPMENT

REPAIRS AND INSURANCE

The burden of keeping a farm in a state of repair is much more often than not shared between landlord and tenant. " Full repairing leases ", where the tenant undertakes to do all, are rare in the farming world. Until the whole matter was clarified in 1948, many a building advanced in decay while the parties disputed whose job it was to tile, glass, point or paint it. Today there is little uncertainty, owing to a twopenny Statutory Instrument entitled The Agriculture (Maintenance, Repair and Insurance of Fixed Equipment) Regulations, 1948, sometimes called the " model clause ".

Many a building advanced in decay while the parties disputed whose job it was . . .

These regulations divide between landlord and tenant the responsibility for maintaining, repairing and insuring the farm's fixed equipment, and lay specified liabilities upon each. " Fixed equipment " embraces a lot more than bricks and mortar. Besides the farmhouse, cottages and buildings it includes roads, gates, fences, hedges, ditches—virtually everything on, in or over the land that is neither the land itself nor crops growing upon it.

9

The parties are still free, if they wish, to ignore the regulations by agreeing their own terms in writing. A written agreement will always include a repair clause, in which the landlord agrees to repair this and that, the tenant t'other and which. But even the best-laid repairs clause may prove to be less than wind- and water-tight: " There isn't a thing here to say I must rethatch the dovecote or replace the staddles to the granary ".

It is in these cases that the regulations come in useful: even more where no written agreement exists. In sum, the position is this: —

Where there is nothing in writing, the regulations apply in their entirety.

Where there is a written agreement which does not cover all the matters in the regulations, the regulations fill the gaps.

Although a repairs clause in an agreement takes priority over the regulations, its position is not impregnable. For where it is substantially different, either party may request the other to agree to alter the existing clause so as to bring it into line with the regulations. If agreement cannot be reached, the matter is referred to an arbitrator.

The arbitrator has to decide whether in all the circumstances the existing terms of the repairs clause are justifiable. If he thinks not, he may vary them accordingly. And if by so doing he imposes on either party a liability previously borne by the other, he may make a consequential adjustment in the rent. To illustrate this point, let us assume that the agreement made the landlord responsible for the farm roads. Now the regulations say that repair of farm roads is the tenant's job. By bringing in the regulations, the arbitrator has shifted the burden for road repairs from landlord to tenant. On the grounds of fair play, therefore, he is entitled to reduce the rent by an amount something like the estimated annual cost of keeping up the roads.

Who does what

The regulations dole out responsibility for repairs and maintenance in the following shares. For simplified reference, the landlord's responsibilities are printed in ordinary type, while *the tenant's responsibilities are printed in italics.*

Farmhouse, cottages and buildings

Tenant generally responsible for keeping them clean and in good tenantable repair, subject to the landlord's specific liabilities as noted below.

Walls

Repair and replace main and exterior walls, including walls of open and covered yards and garden walls. *Interior covering of exterior walls,* unless its bad condition is affected by structural defects in the wall.

Roofs

Repair and replace.
In any one year the tenant pays up to the first £5 in renewing or replacing broken and cracked tiles and slates or replacing slipped ones. Supply straw and reed for thatched roofs.

Eaves-guttering and downpipes

Repair and replace.
The landlord can recover from the tenant one-half of the reasonable cost.
Keep clean and in good working order roof valleys, eaves-guttering, downpipes, gulleys and grease-traps.

Floors, doors and windows

Repair and replace.
Glass, locks and fastenings.
The landlord can recover from the tenant one-half of the reasonable cost.

Fixtures and fittings

Repair, keep clean and in good tenantable repair.

Water supply and sewerage

Repair and replace water mains.
Generally keep water mains in order.
Repair structure of reservoirs or pump houses of water supply system.
Repair pumps.
Repair and replace sewage disposal systems, *except drains.*
Repair drains.
Keep system clean.

Painting

Whenever necessary, and in any case at not more than five-year intervals, paint, gas-tar or creosote outside wood and ironwork, including the inside of external doors and windows which open outwards.

The landlord can recover from the tenant one-half of the reasonable cost of painting, etc., doors windows, eaves-guttering and downpipes.

Whenever necessary, and in any case at not more than seven-year intervals, clean, colour, whiten, paper or paint (depending on what went before) the inside of the farmhouse, cottages and buildings.

The inside of limewashed farm buildings must be limewashed yearly.

Fixed equipment generally

Replace or repair all items of fixed equipment, and do any necessary work to it where it is damaged by the wilful act or negligence of the tenant, his family or his employees.

Hedges, ditches, etc.

Generally keep in repair fences, hedges, walls, posts, stiles, gates. Cut and lay a proper proportion of the hedges in each year.

Watercourses, ponds, ditches and culverts; land drains and outlets.
Roads and bridges. Yards.

The landlord has no liability for buildings, etc., which belong to the tenant. Nor is he liable to execute repairs and replacements rendered necessary by the wilful damage or carelessness of the tenant, his family or his men.

In particular cases, neither party may have any obligation to repair. Every farm has its nondescript building which houses the old tyres they'll use for stack-bottoming, or the crates which will yield eight-and-sixpence apiece if ever there's time to return them empty—a building nothing to look at, but good for as long as the woodworm don't actually meet in the middle. A pound-of-flesh adherence to the regulations would land the parties in for a handsome repair bill; but the liability can be averted by both parties agreeing in writing that the building is obsolete.

To keep each other up to the mark, if the tenant fails to do any repair for which the regulations make him liable, the landlord may write to him saying that such and such needs to be done, and would he kindly go ahead with it. Should the tenant fail to do so within a month, the landlord can see to the repairs himself, and recover the reasonable cost from the tenant forthwith.

The tenant has a similar remedy against the landlord, but in this case three months' notice is allowed. This no more than apparent favouritism is due to the landlord's repairs being in general of a kind that take longer to get done.

INSURANCE

Where a farm is let under a written agreement, provision is usually made for insurance against fire, certainly on the buildings, possibly on some of the tenant's belongings.

Responsibility for insuring the farmhouse, cottages and buildings tends to be undertaken by the landlord. If nothing is set down in writing, the matter is taken care of by the model clause whose main provisions have monopolised this chapter. They lay the burden on the landlord, who is required " to keep the farmhouse, cottages and farm buildings insured to their full value against loss or damage by fire and to execute all works of repair or replacement to the farmhouse, cottages and buildings necessary to make damage by fire, being damage not due to the wilful act or negligence of the tenant ".

That last phrase should be noted. If the farm tenant tosses aside a burning fag-end in the hayloft and the whole building goes up in flames, it modifies the landlord's responsibility to rebuild it. Furthermore, " the landlord shall be under no liability . . . to insure buildings or fixtures which are the property of the tenant ". Lastly, where the parties agree in writing that such and such a building or bit of fixed equipment is obsolete, the landlord may omit it from his fire insurance policy.

We now reveal a somewhat dictatorial facet of the Agricultural Holdings Act. In Chapter 1 we explained that either the landlord or the tenant of a farm can insist on having a written tenancy agreement made, and that whatever else he brings into it an arbitrator called upon to do the job must provide for the nine matters listed in the First Schedule to the Agricultural Holdings Act, 1948. Two of these matters deal with insurance. No. 7 says that the arbitrator must include " a covenant by the landlord in the event of damage by fire to any building . . . to reinstate or replace the building if its reinstatement or replacement is required for the fulfilment of his responsibility to manage the holding in accordance with the rules of good estate management . . . and a covenant by the landlord to insure all such buildings against damage by fire."

No. 8 compels the tenant to insure against fire " all dead stock on the holding " and " harvested crops grown on the holding for consumption thereon ". This compulsion to insure only arises where an arbitrator is appointed to prepare an agreement, or where there is a covenant to that effect in a "mutually agreed" agreement. If the landlord and tenant are content to jog along without anything in writing, the tenant can warm his hands over his burning and uninsured hay, straw and dead stock with a clear, indeed a glowing conscience.

FIXTURES AND IMPROVEMENTS

The distinction between a tenant's fixture and a tenant's improvement is not always immediately apparent. If, for instance, a tenant-farmer mole drains a field, it legally ranks as an improvement.

If he lays on a supply of water to the fields, no one can tell whether it's a fixture or an improvement merely by looking at it. Where it could be either one or the other, its classification depends on certain preliminaries: chiefly, did he get written consent to do the thing before beginning on it ?

Broadly speaking, if the answer is no, the object is a fixture. Otherwise it is an improvement. If a fixed-looking object is legally an improvement, the tenant must leave it alone, but he will get compensation for it on quitting. If it is a fixture, he has certain rights to remove it during or after the run of his tenancy.

The tenant's right to remove fixtures

Here we are unable to offer a comprehensive definition of what objects this right extends to. They must be deduced from the following extract from section 13 of the Agricultural Holdings Act, 1948:

"(a) any engine, machinery, fencing or other fixture affixed to an agricultural holding by the tenant thereof; and

(b) any building (other than one in respect of which the tenant is entitled to compensation . . .) erected by him on the holding."

But it does not extend to fixtures or buildings which the tenant provided because he was under some obligation to do so. For instance, let us say that a stock farmer is taking a 21-year lease of a farm; he would like a new covered yard, but the landlord cannot afford to provide it. The tenant then offers to build it at his own expense, on condition that the landlord accepts a lower rent than he would otherwise have done. A clause is added to the lease making it plain that in consideration of the reduced rent the tenant will erect a covered yard. This is enough to take it out of the tenant's ownership, and it becomes part of the landlord's property accordingly.

Again, a tenant has no proprietary right in, nor any right to compensation for a fixture or building he provides to replace an existing one belonging to the landlord. The farmhouse kitchen may contain a brand new cooker enamelled in eggshell blue provided by the landlord as a welcoming gesture to the farmer's wife. If that lady casts it out and induces her husband to replace it with another in her favourite shade of shocking pink, the new one does not become a tenant's fixture, though the transaction may have cost him dear.

The third principal exception has been hinted at in the above quotation: a building for which the tenant has other rights to compensation. In brief—because the matter is more fully dealt with later in this chapter—supposing the tenant put up or enlarged a building with his landlord's prior written consent, this would emerge as an "improvement", not a fixture. His rights in it would take the form of compensation when, but not before, he quit the farm at the end of the tenancy.

With these exceptions, the tenant has the right, either while the tenancy is running or up to two months after it has ended, to remove any engine, machinery, fencing or other fixture affixed, and any building erected by him on the holding. The Nissen hut to house the battery hens, the pump he bought to boost the water supply before the mains came, the post-and-rail that kept the kiddies from the horsepond before they were old enough to swim: these, when he's done with them, he may remove. But there are three conditions:—

He must warn the landlord, by at least one month's notice in writing, of his intention to remove the fixture or building in question. If the removal is on departing, notice must be given not less than one month before the tenancy ends. During that month the landlord has the right to serve a counter-notice saying that he wishes to buy it himself. If he does so, the tenant forfeits his right to removal; instead, the landlord must pay him its fair value. And if they cannot agree on the value, they appoint an arbitrator to name the sum.

Before removing the fixture the tenant must have paid his rent up to date, and have discharged the other obligations which his agreement and the law lay upon him as tenant. This indeed can be quite a handicap. Strictly speaking it means that, for instance, although he has given up poultry keeping he cannot accept his neighbour's offer for his prefabricated deep-litter house until he has made good the two miles of farm road there never was time to get round to.

Lastly, in removing the fixture or building the tenant must take care to avoid doing any damage than can be avoided. And afterwards he must make good all damage he may have done.

TENANT'S IMPROVEMENTS

These include not only obvious things such as buildings or new roads done by the tenant, but such run-of-the-mill items as liming or putting fertilisers on the land. A complete list of them is included in the Agricultural Holdings Act, 1948. Unlike fixtures which—subject to the ifs and buts just dealt with—the tenant is allowed to remove, these improvements become part and parcel of the farm and may not be taken away. Instead, the tenant has a legal right to be paid compensation for them when he quits at the end of his tenancy.

The list is a longish one, partly because there is some duplication, the reason springing from certain differences in treating those begun before 1st March, 1948, and those begun on or after that date. The reader is more likely to have an active interest in the latter, the so-called New Improvements; but it is worth listing the majority of the Old Improvements for two reasons. First, many farm tenancies still in existence go back to 1948 and earlier, and their present tenants will still have rights to compensation for pre-1948 improvements when they eventually quit. Secondly, the list is referred to in Chapter 5 on Tenant Right Valuations.

Old improvements are set out in the Second Schedule to the 1948 Act, as follows:—

PART I

IMPROVEMENTS FOR WHICH COMPENSATION IS PAYABLE IF CONSENT OF LANDLORD WAS OBTAINED TO THEIR EXECUTION

1. Erection, alteration or enlargement of buildings.
2. Formation of silos.
3. Laying down of permanent pasture.
4. Making and planting of osier beds.
5. Making of water meadows or works of irrigation.
6. Making of gardens.
7. Making or improvement of roads or bridges.
8. Making or improvement of watercourses, ponds, wells or reservoirs or of works for the application of water power or of supply of water for agricultural or domestic purposes.
9. Making or removal of permanent fences.
10. Planting of hops.
11. Planting of orchards or fruit bushes.
12. Protecting young fruit trees.
13. Reclaiming of waste land.
14. Warping or weiring of land.
15. Embankments and sluices against floods.
16. Erection of wirework in hop gardens.
17. Provision of permanent sheep-dipping accommodation.
18. In the case of arable land, the removal of bracken, gorse, tree roots, boulders or other like obstacles to cultivation.

PART II

IMPROVEMENT FOR WHICH COMPENSATION IS PAYABLE IF NOTICE WAS GIVEN TO LANDLORD BEFORE EXECUTION THEREOF

19. Drainage.

Part III of the schedule comprises " improvements for which compensation is payable without either consent of or notice to landlord of their execution ". Being mainly of a short- or medium-term nature, they will by now have been mostly exhausted by the passage of time. We therefore omit them and continue with the Third Schedule to the 1948 Act, which comprises improvements begun on or after 1st March, 1948.

These new improvements fall into three groups, the first two being of a long-term, the third of a short-term nature.

With the first group of long-termers, if they are legally to rank as tenant's improvements and so attract compensation on quitting, the tenant must get the landlord's written consent before starting on them. If the landlord refuses, there is nothing to be done by way of staking a claim to ultimate compensation. They are:—

PART I

1. Making or planting of osier beds.
2. Making of water meadows or works of irrigation.
3. Making of watercress beds.
4. Planting of hops.
5. Planting of orchards or fruit bushes.
6. Warping or weiring of land.
7. Making of gardens.

With respect to those farmers who are born basket-weavers or gardeners, the above have a specialised ring about them; the average landlord would little rejoice at the thought of Dyke Farm subsiding beneath a mantle of watercress. Not that he has an aversion to salad: the fact is that when Dyke Farm falls vacant, he may find himself liable for a high compensation claim for an improvement nobody wants—unless he can find as successor a cress-minded tenant to whom he can transfer the cost. The landlord is given therefore the absolute right to refuse consent.

But with the other group of long-term improvements the tenant has another shot in the locker. For if the landlord refuses consent, or will consent only on terms which the tenant regards as unreasonable, the tenant may carry the matter to the Agricultural Land Tribunal.

After hearing both sides of the question the Tribunal may do one of three things: give approval with no strings attached, or approve subject to conditions, or refuse point blank.

If they decide in the tenant's favour, the landlord has a comeback of sorts. Within one month of receiving notification of the Tribunal's decision, he may serve written notice on them and on the tenant that he proposes to carry out the improvement himself. That being done, he must proceed to do the job within a reasonable time.

There is no definition of " reasonable time ", for while a silo may be thrown up in a week it may take many seasons to reclaim ten acres of waste land. This omission, however, does not give the landlord a licence to stall, for if he fails to keep up to the mark the tenant may apply again to the Tribunal and ask that their original approval should be allowed to proceed.

As far as it affects the tenant's right to compensation for improvements, the Tribunal's approval is equivalent to the landlord's written consent.

Here, to complete the Third Schedule, follows the list of improvements to which the prior consent of the landlord or the approval of the Agricultural Land Tribunal is required.

PART II

8. Erection, alteration or enlargement of buildings, and making or improvement of permanent yards.
9. Construction of silos.
10. Claying of land.
11. Marling of land.
12. Making or improvement of roads or bridges.
13. Making or improvement of watercourses, culverts, ponds, wells or reservoirs, or of works for the application of water power for agricultural or domestic purposes or for the supply of water for such purposes.
14. Making or removal of permanent fences.
15. Reclaiming of waste land.
16. Making or improvement of embankments or sluices.
17. Erection of wirework for hop gardens.
18. Provision of permanent sheep-dipping accommodation.
19. Removal of bracken, gorse, tree roots, boulders or other like obstacles to cultivation.
20. Land drainage (other than mole drainage) and works carried out to secure the efficient functioning thereof.
21. Provision or laying-on of electric light or power.
22. Provision of means of sewage disposal.
23. Repairs to fixed equipment, being equipment reasonably required for the proper farming of the holding, other than repairs which the tenant is under an obligation to carry out.
24. The growth of herbage crops for commercial seed production.

The short-term improvements, comprised in the Fourth Schedule, are seven in number. Mostly of an everyday farming nature, they require neither the landlord's nor anyone else's consent. If the tenant wishes to mole drain, or lime, stuff his cattle with purchased oilcake, even burn clay, he may do so without asking and thereby sow the seeds of a possible claim on departure. Because they are so closely associated with tenant right valuations, it is convenient to carry them forward to Chapter 5. For allied reasons, the method of compensating a tenant for long-term improvements is taken up in the same place.

FIXED EQUIPMENT DIRECTIONS

If this chapter so far has given the impression that the tenant is the main provider of additions, both great and small, to the holding he farms, it has completely distorted the picture. Nine-point-something times out of ten the big improvements—the buildings, the laying on of water or power—are done by the landlord. Nine-point-something times out of ten they are done at the tenant's request, with goodwill and co-operation on both sides.

In specific cases, where the point-something landlord refuses to play at all, the tenant may invoke section 4 of the Agriculture Act, 1958, and get the Agricultural Land Tribunal to apply the spur.

These cases arise where the tenant is faced with statutory obligations imposed by, for instance, the Milk and Dairies Regulations (see Chapter 12) or the various regulations relating to the safety, health and welfare of farm workers (Chapter 16). If to comply with such regulations means that new fixed equipment is essential, or that existing equipment must be altered or repaired, the tenant may apply to the Tribunal for a direction that his landlord should do the necessary work. In his application he must specify, among other things, the nature of his agricultural activity.

The Tribunal have to satisfy themselves on a number of matters. Is it reasonable—taking into account his responsibility to farm in accordance with the rules of good husbandry—that the tenant should carry on the form of agricultural activity specified in his application to them ? If so, supposing the fixed equipment he asks for is refused, will he be contravening requirements ?

Even if the answer is yes in both cases, there are grounds for refusal. Thus, the tenant must show that the agricultural activity on which his case relies has been going on for at least three years prior to the date of his application, unless it involves no substantial change in the established farming system. For example, if six months ago there wasn't a cow on the place, he cannot now apply for a direction to make the landlord convert the old granary into a milking parlour. Again, it may be that the landlord had other plans for the farm. Perhaps the landlord can convince the Tribunal that he was far advanced in a scheme for readjusting the boundaries of the farms on his estate and amalgamating them into more farmable units. If so, it would be to nobody's lasting advantage to spend a thousand or two on a pint-sized holding destined to be absorbed into its neighbouring farm.

Finally, there is no power for the Tribunal to give a direction about fixed equipment where the responsibilities are already laid down. If, say, a tenancy agreement required the tenant to repair and maintain the floor of the milking parlour, and through his neglect it degenerated into a standing pond, he could not through the Tribunal shift the burden on to the landlord, even though he had no money to expend in bringing it up to the standard required by the Milk and Dairies Regulations.

Chapter 3

FRUITS OF THE SOIL

CROPPING AND SELLING

Freedom of cropping

Our farming forebears were great ones for crop rotations. For centuries whole parishes were farmed in common under the open field system, with its unvarying three-year cycle: spring corn this year, autumn corn the next, then fallow. In the mid-eighteenth century change came about with the introduction of turnips as a

spring corn this year ·· Autumn corn next · · · Then fallow

farm crop and of " artificial " grasses, until presently the four-course rotation—wheat, roots, barley, seeds—spread far and away from its birthplace on the light lands of Norfolk and established itself as the basis of every progressive cropping system.

Thereafter on letting a farm the agreement would normally include a clause which bound the tenant to crop the arable land on a specified rotation and so leave it at the termination of the tenancy. Many existing agreements indeed still contain some such provisions, purporting not only to bind the tenant to a rigorous rotation, but prohibiting him from selling any hay, straw or manure produced on the farm.

In fact, section 11 of the Agricultural Holdings Act, 1948, allows a tenant to disregard much of these restrictions, so that he may be the judge of the best way of farming his holding. No matter what his agreement may say, he can crop the arable land—only the arable land, mind; there are separate provisions relating to permanent pasture—in any rotation he pleases. This does not,

21

however, apply to the last year of the tenancy, for then he must
bring the land round so as to leave it in the agreed rotation, unless
he agrees with the landlord in writing to one different from the
original.

In exercising this freedom of cropping, the tenant is obliged to
take steps " to protect the holding from injury or deterioration ".
That is to say, he must not abuse the privilege. If, for instance, he
continued to grow wheat year after year on a field where take-all
multiplied, he would manifestly be letting the holding down, and
the law would cease to encourage his enterprise.

Where a tenant by overmuch freedom of cropping has injured
the farm—or looks likely to bring about its deterioration—the
landlord has two remedies, and two only:—

(a) He may apply to the County Court for an injunction
restraining the tenant from continuing that particular mal-
practice.

(b) In any case he may recover damages for the harm done, but
not until the tenancy comes to an end.

The tenant may argue, of course, that whatever the landlord
thinks he shouldn't be doing is not really hurting the farm. In such
event the matter is submitted to arbitration, and the arbitrator's
award counts as conclusive proof one way or the other.

Selling off produce

Long before oilcake and fertilisers came about, most if not all
of the farmer's limited products were grown for home consumption: wheat and barley for him and his family, hay and straw for
cattle and sheep. An agreement for letting a farm customarily
provided that the tenant should never at any time sell off hay,
straw, roots or manure. A reasonable enough provision, for the
maintenance of fertility depended mainly on muck, and if " muck
was the mother of money " it was fathered by just that traditional
home-grown fare. Muck, it was maintained, belonged to the land,
so to sell off the source of it amounted to robbery.

The availability of fertilisers changed most of that philosophy.
The potential nitrogen, phosphate and potash removed from the
farm on the sale of a ton of hay could be replaced from the
imported bag, and the farmer who fell for the sovereign's clink
when the carriage folk sent James to barter for hay for the hosses
was more to be envied than censured.

So it is that, no matter what restrictions a tenancy agreement may
place upon the disposal of his produce, a tenant may sell off,
exchange or give away any crops he grows on the farm. But again,
as with his freedom of cropping rights, this does not apply to the
last year of the tenancy, when he must obey the terms of his

agreement, and either feed, or leave for the next tenant to take over, whatever hay, straw and roots (and occasionally other specified crops) he has produced in the last twelve months.

The right to sell off does not at any time apply to farmyard manure, unless the landlord concurs.

In order to protect the holding, where the tenant exercises his rights of free marketing, he must make arrangements to return to the land the equivalent manurial value of whatever stuff the agreement says he musn't sell off and the law says he may. In fact, the manurial value of hay and the rest is not high, and very much more than the equivalent is returned in the normal course of fertilising the next crop.

The landlord's remedies against abuse are the same as above, where a tenant is over-free with his cropping.

PERMANENT PASTURE

The tenant's rights to disregard would-be restrictions on his choice of cropping apply only to the arable land on the farm. In most tenancy agreements there will be a clause requiring him to maintain certain fields, sometimes a certain proportion of the total acreage, as permanent pasture. This again harks back to the days of yore—and not, in fact, as yore as all that—when permanent pasture was held in such reverence that merely to draw a home-bound plough across it was an affront to agriculture.

Particularly during and since the war farming opinion has encouraged the short-term ley as a more fruitful alternative, and taking the plough round the whole farm is no longer the worst form of husbandry. However, if a tenant has covenanted not to break up the Home Meadow, Pensioner's Pasture, Maypole Green and the rest of his picturesquely named pastures scheduled as "permanent", he cannot flagrantly do so without laying himself open to penalties. What he can do is to submit the matter to arbitration.

No doubt he will first discuss the matter with his landlord with a view to getting his written consent to override that clause in the agreement. Whether or not he makes this preliminary approach, section 10 of the 1948 Act allows him to serve a notice on the landlord demanding a reference to arbitration as to " whether it is expedient in order to secure the full and efficient farming of the holding that the amount of land required to be maintained as permanent pasture should be reduced ".

If, after the usual enquiries, discussions, inspection and deliber-ation, the arbitrator makes up his mind that it would be a good thing for the tenant to plough up some or all of the permanent pasture, he duly says so. In his award he may also add incidental directions which alter the cropping clause in the agreement.

All this may appear hard on the landlord, for two reasons. First, on most farms the rental value per acre of permanent pasture is reckoned to be higher than that of arable land. Secondly, as part of his tenant right on quitting, the tenant may claim compensation for the cost of laying land down to grass. To give an extreme example, if a tenant took over a farm all under permanent grass (for the value of which he would pay nothing over and above the rent), ploughed it all up with an arbitrator's blessing, and sowed it down before quitting, the landlord would be obliged to pay him for it as "tenant's pasture".

The mitigating answer to that one is that the law gives the arbitrator a right to order that when the tenant comes to quit the farm he shall leave behind, free of compensation, an area of permanent pasture—or of temporary pasture sown with a specified seeds mixture—such compensation-free grassland not to exceed the acreage he was allowed to plough up.

RIGHTS TO GAME

In Part VI of this book we deal with the game laws in general. Here we deal only with the subject as it concerns landlord and tenant.

The fundamental law is that if nothing in writing is agreed to the contrary, all rights to kill and take the game go with the occupation of the farm that harbours them. In such cases the landlord may not shoot over the land without the tenant's leave. If he does, he is committing trespass.

In tenancy agreements, however, it is very usual to insert a clause " reserving unto the landlord all game and wild fowl ", including their nests and eggs, to say nothing of foxes and fish, coupled with the exclusive right to himself, his friends and his sporting tenants to range over the farm in pursuit of the same.

There is one right which cannot be denied the tenant, namely to kill and take hares and rabbits. Legally these are *ground game,* and although the landlord may include both in the sporting clause, he cannot claim exclusive rights in them: he merely shares the right with the tenant.

The occupier of the farm may kill and take the ground game himself, or he may authorise (in writing) other people to do so on his behalf. The choice of persons he may authorise is limited to members of his household resident on the farm, employees in his ordinary service, and one other person hired by him for reward. There is a further restriction in that only the occupier himself and one other to whom he gives written authority may kill hares and rabbits with firearms. In an all-out attack, therefore, if he and the head cowman are equipped with guns, then Mum, Uncle Bill, the youngsters, the farm staff and Harold the crypto-poacher must confine themselves to such non-explosive weapons as sticks, nets, catapults and bare hands.

If the sporting rights are not reserved to the landlord, the tenant may let them to sporting tenants for money or love, provided he has not agreed to the contrary.

Damage by game

Few farmers have time to begrudge the odd ear or two of corn to the questing pheasant. But the case is altered when, in a " smashing good year for the birds ", he sees half his crop going down their crops and has signed away his right to take reprisals. Fortunately, section 14 of the 1948 Act gives redress in the form of a claim for compensation for damage by game.

" Game " for this purpose means deer, pheasants, partridges, grouse and black game. And a claim can only arise where the rights to kill these five species are reserved to the landlord, and the landlord has not handed them back by, for instance, giving the tenant a licence to kill all or any of them. And the claim must exceed one shilling per acre. (It would surely require skill, at present-day values, to prove less, even though that shilling an acre is based on the area actually damaged, not spread over the whole farm !)

The tenant must give his landlord written notice within one month of being made aware of the damage—or indeed of the time when he ought reasonably to have become aware of it. The landlord must then be allowed an opportunity to make his inspection. If the claim is in respect of a growing crop, he must be given a chance to see it before it is cut. If already reaped, e.g., where a stooked field of wheat has been or is being consumed on the premises, he will need to inspect it before it is removed from the land.

Next, the tenant must let the landlord have a detailed account of the damage claimed. The time limit for this is " within one month after the expiration of the calendar year ". So that if the game damage occurred in July 1962, the written claim would have to be submitted not later than 31st January, 1963. Alternatively, the landlord and tenant may agree to some other period, up to twelve months, beyond which no claim may be entertained. If the claim cannot be mutually agreed, the only way compensation may be settled is by arbitration.

Where the landlord has reserved the game rights but let them to a sporting tenant, the farm tenant still makes his claim directly against his landlord.

To say that the above covers the " every day " cases of damage by game might suggest that such claims are common. They are not. Even a curmudgeonly farmer has been known to waive his strict rights when now and again he is offered a day with the guns. It is equally disarming when the odd brace of partridges is delivered bearing a cordial label " With Compliments ". We use the word, therefore, to contrast the farmer's remedy under Act of Parliament with another, less cut and dried, situation.

Normally neither landlord nor anyone else is liable to compensate a farmer for damage caused by the *natural* increase of game which are already on his farm. But there have been occasions where game has been brought on the land in large numbers, or reared on adjoining land in such quantities, as to become a menace to the neighbouring farmer. The farmer's rights in such circumstances were laid down in a case heard in 1885 (*Farrer v. Nelson*). The landlord let a farm, reserved the sporting rights and let them to a shooting tenant. In a wood next to the farm, but not part of it, pheasants multiplied in excessive numbers and voraciously fed on the farmer's corn. He brought an action and recovered damages from the sporting tenant. The moral of that was laid down thus: " A person is entitled to bring on his land any quantity of game which can reasonably and properly be kept on it, so that nothing extraordinary and non-natural is done . . . but the moment he brings on game to an unreasonable amount, or causes it to increase to an unreasonable extent, he is doing that which is unlawful, and an action may be maintained by his neighbour for the damage which he has sustained."

TREES AND TIMBER

There cannot be many farms in this country, let or unlet, which are entirely treeless. Sometimes within the ring fence there will be flourishing plantations; there may be shelter belts intentionally planted for the purpose; while many quickthorn hedges offer house-room to the isolated elm or walnut.

What legal rights the tenant has in trees growing on the farm depend, in the first place, on what his agreement says. If there is an agreement it may well contain a clause reserving to the landlord " all timber and timberlike trees and trees likely to become timber and all other trees whatsoever standing or being upon the premises, with liberty to the landlord to fell, cut, convert and carry away the same ". In such event the tenant is obviously very tightly restricted.

But where the landlord has made no such provision the tenant is in a stronger—though not, perhaps, very strong—position. Before setting out his rights, a distinction must be made between trees that are legally " timber " and those which are not.

The general law recognises oak, ash and elm as timber trees, provided they are 20 years old and more but not too old to contain a reasonable quantity of usable wood in them, sufficient to make a good post. These three species constitute timber all over the country. In more limited areas other trees as well count as timber, according to local custom as backed up by legal decisions. For example, beech is a timber tree in Buckinghamshire, Gloucestershire and parts of Bedfordshire, Hampshire and Surrey. Birch is timber in Cumberland and Yorkshire. In other localities at various times law cases have held to be timber trees aspen, blackthorn, cherry, crab-apple, holly, hornbeam, horse-chestnut, lime, walnut, whitethorn, willow and yew. (The forester, the botanist, merely the plain countryman with an eye for trees will have spotted that all these are hardwood trees. The law has never recognised pines, larches, firs—indeed any so-called softwood or coniferous trees—as timber.)

That distinction made, we return to the tenant who has nothing in writing to say what he can and cannot do about trees on his farm. His rights and wrongs are these:

He may take and enjoy the fruit, shelter and shade of all the trees growing on the land; the landlord has no right to touch them.

He may harvest and sell the coppice and underwood, provided he cuts them reasonably, that is to say at proper age and in a husbandlike manner.

He may cut down, and use or sell, trees of any age which will spring up again from the stools, except timber trees, fruit trees, trees planted for shelter or ornament, or trees which hold up river banks and the like. (In practice there are few valuable or useful trees likely to pass all these tests !)

He may take timber for the repair of his house (provided he is liable for such work), for the repair of gates and fences, and for the repair of his farm implements.

He may fell dead trees and take the wood.

If he holds the farm on a long lease, it is probable that he is entitled to thin the growing plantations in due time and sell or keep the thinnings.

He may take windfalls of decayed timber trees and of all trees not timber; but windfalls of sound timber belong to the landlord.

The landlord who omits to reserve the trees is considerably at the tenant's mercy. Where the timber trees are concerned a deadlock may come about. True, they remain the landlord's property and the tenant cannot fell or sell them. On the other hand, the landlord cannot go on the farm to do anything to them without the tenant's permission.

MINES AND MINERALS

The soil of Britain and what lies beneath contain something like 40 minerals, from clay to coal, which are profitable to work. Most of them are at the disposal of the landowner, who may work them himself or let them to others. There are some exceptions. Gold, silver and platinum belong to the crown, while coal is vested in the National Coal Board. Apart from these, and for our purposes, the term " minerals " legally includes every substance which can be got from underneath the surface of the earth for the purpose of profit. Note the word " underneath "; the surface itself is for farming. By extension, a " mine " is an underground excavation for getting minerals.

As with the other amenities filling this chapter, where a farm is let under a written agreement, almost always it reserves to the landlord " all mines, minerals, quarries, stones, sand, brickearth, clay ", etc., etc., together with " liberty to search for and remove the same and let down the surface of the land ". This of course puts an end to the tenant's ambition to offset his farming loss by the sale of bricks or china clay.

Where there is no such reservation, the tenant may work existing mines and quarries, but he may not open new ones.

Rights of support

A right of support has long been recognised as one of the " natural rights " associated with the ownership of land at common law. Thus an owner-occupier would be entitled to bring an action for damages in trespass against a mining company which, in the course of mining operations underneath adjoining land, inadvertently let down the surface of his land so as to cause damage. Where land is let for an agricultural tenancy, the landlord is under a general obligation not to do anything fundamentally inconsistent with the tenant-farmer's right to what is usually called " quiet possession ". Unless he reserved an express right to do so, a landlord of an agricultural holding would not be entitled to grant a series of mining leases which would inevitably involve the letting down of the surface and consequent interference with drainage.

Almost invariably, however, a tenancy agreement contains an express reservation of mineral rights, and this sometimes includes an express right to let down the surface of the land. If the agreement merely reserves the mineral rights without reserving an express right to let down the surface, then the landlord would probably be liable for any damage resulting from subsidence if he afterwards granted a mineral lease. It has been held (in *Butter-knowle Colliery Company v. Bishop Auckland Industrial Co-operative Company*, 1906) that the mere fact of giving a right to sink pits and to work and get minerals is not sufficient to deprive the surface owner of his common law right of support. We think the same reasoning would apply to a reservation of rights—as opposed to a grant.

Where the landlord has expressly reserved the right to let down the surface, there may be an express provision for compensation to the tenant for any damage which he may suffer as a result. If there is no such express provision for compensation, then the 1948 Act contains no guidance as to the position. A court would presumably look at the general tenor of the agreement to decide whether or not the parties intended that the tenant should be compensated for damage arising from subsidence.

Chapter 4

THE TENTH POINT OF THE LAW

" Possession is nine points of the law " is a legal maxim which has become a common proverb. It implies that where a person is in possession of property—be it a farm, a beach hut or a portable wireless—the assumption is that he has a right to possess it. That right continues unless and until another person can prove a better title to it.

In this chapter we assemble the legal ways in which that other person, in our case the landlord, can recover possession of the farm he owns.

ENTRY

On letting any form of property to a tenant, the basic rule is that the landlord must keep off the premises. Section 17 of the Agricultural Holdings Act, 1948, makes three exceptions to this basic rule. It says that a landlord, or anyone authorised by him, may enter on the holding at all reasonable times:—
  (a) to inspect its condition;
  (b) to fulfil his responsibilities to manage the farm properly;
  (c) to provide or improve fixed equipment, apart from what might be entailed under (b).

There is no definition of " all reasonable times ", but it may be assumed that an attempt to begin re-roofing the farmhouse while the tenant was in the throes of lambing, his wife prostrate after spring cleaning, the children in quarantine for chickenpox, and Granny glued to a late-night repeat of These You Will Love, would justify a request to defer it at least until daylight tomorrow.

As to the reasons, only a guilt-ridden tenant could find them unreasonable. Every letting, we have seen, lays on the tenant an obligation to farm the land tolerably well. Nor need he feel spied upon if now and again the landlord or his agent wanders over to see how things are going.

The second cause lies in the landlord's responsibilities "to manage the holding according to the rules of good estate management". The rules of good husbandry we outline on page 39. Broadly speaking, the corresponding rules of good estate management require a landlord to manage his land in such a way that an average tenant could farm it efficiently, and in particular to pro-

31

vide the fixed equipment necessary for that purpose. No matter
how large the invasion of surveyors, architects, builders, delivery
men, clerks of works and the like, not many tenants would cry
"Trespass!" with the prospect of a new range of buildings in
view. Nevertheless, if only to frustrate those few, the landlord's
rights of entry have been laid down by statute.

The third cause largely fills in any gaps in the second. It
authorises the landlord or people working for him to visit the farm,
for the purpose of providing or improving fixed equipment on it,
"otherwise than in fulfilment" of his good estate management
responsibilities.

A supplement might be added to these three cases. In discussing
the effect of the repairs regulations we remarked (page 12) that
if a tenant fails to do any repairs for which they make him liable,
the landlord can do them and pass on the expense. Here we have
a fourth reason for which the landlord has a statutory right to
invade the tenant's privacy.

All these are the rights of every farm landlord. In previous
chapters we have given a number of purposes for which the landlord may enter a farm—for sporting, for felling timber, for getting
minerals, etc. These rights come about only by written agreement
with the tenant, and there need be no end to them. Many clauses
reserve to the landlord the power to enter the farm to do this,
that and those, and "for all other reasonable purposes".

RE-ENTRY

This is a way by which a landlord can put an end to a tenancy
without resorting to notice to quit. It does not mean what it seems
to, that he actually, physically steps on to the farm. In fact,
re-entry is arranged through a legal action. It is also spoken of as
"forfeiture", a more meaningful term.

A right to re-enter arises only when a tenancy agreement contains
a clause which expressly says that the landlord may re-enter
immediately and terminate the tenancy where the tenant has done
some specific wrong, notably that he has failed to fulfil his
obligations under the agreement. Whereas forfeiture clauses are
very common indeed, in practice they are rarely put into effect.
Supposing, for example, the clause gives the landlord a right to
re-enter "if any part of the rent is in arrear for thirty days", and
the tenant does omit to pay it in time, not many landlords would
dream of invoking their forfeiture rights. In any event none would
be entitled to walk on to the farm and take possession without
ceremony. First he would have to apply to the court; and in the
exercise of its discretion the court would likely refuse forfeiture
if the tenant's breach of covenant were insubstantial. In short, the
landlord would need a strong case to succeed.

NOTICE TO QUIT

Twelve months' notice required

Farming being an unhurried occupation—the townsman, in his ignorance, may go so far as to call it leisurely—the farm he runs is not the kind of thing a tenant wishes to be jostled into or out of. When he does come to quit, a whole year is none too long to get everything cleared up: the cropping left in proper rotation, the neglected repairs put right, and possibly the move to another farm arranged.

A whole year is none too long to get everything cleared up.

Section 23 of the 1948 Act plays for time by insisting that at least twelve months' notice to quit must be given, whether it is the landlord wishing to get possession or the tenant himself wishing to move out. This applies both to those tenancies which otherwise run on indefinitely from year to year and to leases for two years or more.

Where the farm is let on a lease for two years or more, the *longest* notice that may be given is two years. For example, supposing a tenant has a 21-year lease which is due to expire on 25th March, 1964. If he decides that he would like to give up on that day, it is not enough merely to sit back and wait. He must serve a written notice to that effect not earlier than 25th March, 1962, and not later than 25th March, 1963. If he serves it on, say, 20th March, 1962, the position can be remedied (provided he spots it in time!) by waiting not less than five days before sending another. But if he delays until after 25th March, 1963, it is too late until another year. In that case, when the lease ends on 25th March, 1964, a year to year tenancy begins.

A handful of exceptions qualify this rule, and a shorter than 12-months' notice may be given where: —

(1) The tenant has gone bankrupt (see p. 40).

(2) The landlord wants the land for some non-agricultural purpose. But he must have made prophetic provision for this in the agreement, and he must have specified the purpose. For instance, in the agreement the tenant may have promised to quit the Potter's Field at the end of six months' notice should his landlord wish to build a house on it for himself. This is a specific purpose, and a non-agricultural one, and six months' notice is all in order. Supposing, however, the landlord changed his mind and served six months' notice to quit the Potter's Field to build a squash court on it, it would not work.

(3) Notice is given by a tenant to his sub-tenant. If there is no agreement to the contrary (there usually is), a tenant farmer can sublet his farm to another, known as the sub-tenant. But even though he moves to New Zealand the original (or " head ") tenant is under obligations to his landlord as long as their agreement runs. One of those obligations is to give up possession when the tenancy ends.

Just how short a length of notice will do in these exceptional cases depends first on what is said in the agreement. If nothing is said, the general rule is that half a year's notice is required to terminate a yearly tenancy.

Security of tenure

In 1948, the law introduced a number of safeguards to protect the reasonably-behaving tenant-farmer who receives notice to quit but does not wish to leave. The rules and procedures are not easy to grasp in the actual words of sections 24 and on of the Agricultural Holdings Act, and in some ways the following is over-simplified. We will first summarise it, then look a bit deeper.

This, then, is the situation in outline.

1. If a landlord serves notice to quit, the tenant may within one month of its service serve a counter-notice objecting to it.

2. In that event, the notice will not be valid unless the Agricultural Land Tribunal give their consent to it.

3. The A.L.T. may give consent *only* for a limited number of reasons.

4. There are seven cases in which the tenant cannot object to the notice.

Objecting to the notice

The procedure is quite straightforward. Within one month of the date on which the landlord serves (i.e., gives) notice to quit,

the tenant replies with a counter-notice in something like these
words:—

> I hereby give you counter-notice that I require subsection (1)
> of section 24 of the Agricultural Holdings Act, 1948, to apply
> to the notice to quit dated 10th September last served upon me
> in respect of Coldacre Farm in the Parish of Icing in the
> County of Bergshire which I hold of you as tenant.

The tenant's invocation of section 24 puts upon the landlord the
onus of formally requesting the Agricultural Land Tribunal to give
their consent to the notice. He must do so within one month of
the date of the counter-notice. Otherwise the tenant may ignore
the landlord's original notice.

The A.L.T. intervene

There is a strict limit to the variety of reasons for which the
Tribunal may consent to the landlord's notice. These are set out
in section 25 of the Act as amended by the Agriculture Act, 1958.
If none of them applies, the landlord is wasting his time in attempt-
ing to enlist the A.L.T.'s interest. His case must be based on one
or more of these grounds:—

(a) That consent to the notice is in the interests of good hus-bandry.

In this respect the landlord must convince the Tribunal that he
wants to relet the holding to someone who will farm it better than
the present tenant. Alternatively, if he intends to take it in hand
himself, he must prove that his proposed farming system, plan of
management, capital available, and so on and so forth will pretty
certainly show an improvement over the way the place is being
farmed at present. It is not his task to show that the tenant is a
bad farmer: that is a separate matter we shall come to in discussing certificates of bad husbandry.

(b) That consent is in the interests of sound management.

This may sound no different from the last, but there is one clear
distinction. " Good husbandry " applies to the farming of the land
to which the notice relates looked at as a separate farm. " Sound
management " refers to the management of the whole estate of
which the farm is but a part. As a typical instance, the landlord
might give notice to quit the whole or a part of Parson's Farm
with a view to adding it to the adjoining Park Farm. He must
then convince the Tribunal that the enlarged farm will be a more
economic farming proposition.

Sound management involves looking at the whole estate and each
part of it, but it does not take into account the attributes of the
tenant from whom the land is taken, or the effect of doing so upon
his personal conditions and fortunes as a farmer (*Evans v. Roper*,
1960).

(c) That the land is required for agricultural research or education or for smallholdings or allotments.

Research and education are normally the province of public bodies, but if a landlord could convince the Tribunal that his proposal to treble the lamb crop by floodlighting the farm is at least worth experiment, he might be entitled to recover possession of the farm as a private individual.

(d) That greater hardship would be caused by withholding than by giving consent to the notice.

This, it may be imagined, is a tricky matter to substantiate, and offers scope for all manner of facts and fancies whereby the Tribunal may be moved to tears. Perhaps we should do best to quote a far from imaginary case, where a landowner bought two farms, amounting to 200 acres, to establish his son and daughter in farming. At the time of purchase he believed that the sitting tenant would be leaving. The tenant did in fact acquire another farm three miles away, to which he moved himself and his dairying activities; but on receiving notice to quit the original farm he challenged it.

The owner submitted to the Agricultural Land Tribunal that the tenant was not making full and proper use of the holding. He himself was having to make do with only 21 acres, which offered inadequate scope for his children's livelihood. Nevertheless, his daughter had built up a small dairy herd, with pigs and poultry as a sideline.

The Tribunal found that, what with the daughter's farm institute training and the son's National Diploma in Agriculture, they had had a sound background and seemed capable of managing the holding. In view of this, and of the fact that they planned to farm on the spot whereas the tenant proposed to run it from the other farm, they felt that in the interests of sound management the landlord's proposal should operate. As to hardship, in their view it would not substantially fall on the tenant on account of the income he derived from the other farm. To withhold consent would upset the career of the owner's son and daughter; it would mean either tying up the landlord's capital or selling the farm in the hope of buying one elsewhere with vacant possession, which he could ill afford. Greater hardship would therefore be caused by withholding consent to the notice to quit. The Tribunal decided in consequence that it should be allowed to operate.

(e) Where the land is required for a non-agricultural use for which planning consent either (i) is needed but has not been obtained, or (ii) is not necessary.

The only practical application of this appears to be the case where the landlord requires the land for forestry. This is strictly not agriculture, but planning permission nevertheless is not required for it. The paragraph might conceivably enable the Tribunal to consent to the notice to quit taking effect where a landlord intends to use the farm for, say, private house building but has not yet got planning permission; but we seriously doubt whether the Tribunal would grant possession in such an instance. This is because the Act specifically gives the landlord a right to get possession when the land is required for a non-agricultural use for which planning permission has already been granted, as we shall presently see.

General proviso

Many cases submitted to the Agricultural Land Tribunal resolve themselves into six of one and half a dozen of the other. No matter on which of the five grounds the application is based, nor how powerful the landlord's case, there is a general overriding provision which the Tribunal are bound to take into consideration. In short, they must withhold consent to the operation of the notice to quit if " in all the circumstances it appears to them that a fair and reasonable landlord would not insist on possession ".

No sort of rules can be devised to guide the Tribunal or the parties who appear before them on this point, any more than " greater hardship " is capable of a cut and dried definition. Supposing, however, that Blackacre Farm had been tenanted these past 12 years by sound, steady, hardworking Mr. Ten-sacks-to-the-acre. The landlord wishes to let Blackacre to Mr. Twenty-sacks, an exceptional neighbour with green fingers and one of everything from the Massey-Brownfield catalogue. He argues before the Tribunal that to replace Mr. Ten by Mr. Twenty would be in the interests of good husbandry. On the face of it, Mr. Twenty might justifiably claim to be a better husbandman than Mr. Ten. On the face of it, too, Blackacre might respond to that much extra fer-tiliser, tillage and green-fingery which Mr. Twenty would bestow upon it. And yet, all in all, considering the solid capabilities of Mr. Ten, and the fact that he would suffer undeniable hardship by being turned out (even though " greater hardship " had not been evoked), surely if Mr. Ten's point of view were put nicely to a landlord who listened patiently and sympathetically, he would not *insist* on getting possession? If there is any doubt, the landlord's application must fail.

Furthermore, where the Tribunal do give their go-ahead to a notice to quit, they may impose conditions to ensure that the land-lord does in fact use the farm for the purpose he bases his applica-tion upon. If the landlord does not comply with those conditions the Tribunal may impose a penalty upon him, in the form of a sum of up to two years' rent of the farm or of the part to which the notice to quit refers.

Finally, where the Tribunal consent to a notice to quit, they have power to postpone the termination date of the tenancy, for up to 12 months, in cases where it would operate within six months after the date they gave such consent. They may do this either off their own bat, or at the tenant's request. In the latter event the tenant must make a formal application within 14 days of the Tribunal's consent to the notice.

The Seven Deadly Sins

So far we have been dealing with the basic rule: landlord serves notice, tenant objects, Tribunal decide. There are, however, certain cases where the tenant has no right to object to the notice to quit. They appear in section 24 of the 1948 Act and they are seven in number; and since most of them spring from the tenant's misbehaviour they are sometimes referred to as the seven deadly sins.

Provided the landlord states in the notice that it is being given on one of the following grounds, the tenant is nonplussed.

(a) Where a landlord has obtained the Agricultural Land Tribunal's consent to the notice before it is served.

This appears similar to the rigmarole we have just described; and so indeed it is. The difference is in the relative positions of the horse and the cart. Previously, notice to quit came first, followed by a call on the Tribunal. Here the Tribunal's consent precedes the notice.

Once again the Tribunal may only give consent for one of the five reasons considered above, coupled with the proviso about a fair and reasonable landlord not insisting on possession. The landlord has to apply to the Tribunal not less than three and not more than 12 months before the one year's notice to quit begins to operate.

(b) Where the land is wanted for some non-agricultural purpose for which planning consent has been obtained.

This links up with the power of the Tribunal to grant possession where the land is required for non-agricultural purposes which do not need planning consent, or which do but have not yet received it. The difference here is that planning consent *has* been obtained, in which case the Tribunal are not concerned.

The landlord must possess some evidence to prove that the land really is required for the non-agricultural purpose; e.g., that having got planning permission to smother his farm with a glue factory, he honestly intends to put his scheme into practice.

In many cases it may be that the landlord needs no more than part of the farm for his non-agricultural purpose. Though normally notice to quit part of a farm, or any other premises, is void at

common law, it has been held that a notice to quit part of a farm
on this ground is valid—this in spite of the fact that the Act refers
simply to " the land ", which might at first sight suggest that the
landlord's right applied only where planning permission had been
granted in respect of the whole farm.

(c) Where the landlord has got a certificate of bad husbandry against the tenant.

Few farm tenants, and no good farmer-tenants, could quarrel
with this provision, which allows the landlord to rid himself of one
who isn't doing his duty by the land. There is often a narrow
borderline between the indifferent tenant and the rank bad 'un, and
while a field of poppies may make the perfectionist landlord see
red, more tolerant judgment might recognise it as something less
than a hanging matter.

In the interest of impartiality the issue is given to the Agricultural
Land Tribunal to decide, and the procedure is subject to strict
time limits. The landlord's application to the A.L.T. for a certificate of bad husbandry must be made not more than six months
before serving notice to quit on those grounds. Put the other way,
notice to quit must be given not more than six months after the
application for (not the grant of) the certificate; but it cannot be
served until the certificate is actually given.

To give a ruling on a matter where opinion may be divided, there
needs to be some yardstick to go by. Consequently the law has
devised its own " rules of good husbandry ", in section 11 of the
Agriculture Act, 1947, and to show that a tenant is farming badly
he must be proved to have contravened one or more of them.
Good husbandry has regard to the extent to which:—

  (i) the permanent pasture is being treated and managed;
 (ii) the arable land is being cropped and cared for;
(iii) on a stock-farm, the herds and flocks are being properly
      managed and the numbers kept up;
 (iv) the crops and livestock are being kept free from diseases
      and pests;
  (v) the gathered crops are stored and protected;
 (vi) maintenance and repairs are carried out.

(d) Where the tenant has failed to pay rent or remedy some breach of covenant capable of remedy.

These sins are not sins until brought to the tenant's attention.
Where he is behind with his rent, the landlord must serve him with
a written notice to pay up within two months. Where he has
committed a breach of his tenancy agreement which can be
remedied, the landlord must serve a notice requiring him, within
a specified or " reasonable " time, to put the matter right. Only
when the time has run out and the matter is still to be seen to can

the landlord serve notice to quit " on the grounds that you failed to comply with my written demand, dated 1st July, to pay the sum of £120 being rent due at Lady Day last " or " to repair the fence adjoining Oliver's Field by Midsummer day."

(e) Where the tenant has committed some breach of covenant incapable of remedy.

Most breaches of covenant can be remedied. The blocked ditch, the prostrate fence, can be scoured and propped upright. The cottage window can be reglazed, the cowhouse limewashed. The tenant who covenanted in his lease " to reside in the farmhouse " can throw out his mother-in-law and creep back from the sanctuary of the caravan.

Other breaches cannot be so remedied, and provided they have " materially prejudiced " the landlord's interest in the farm, they may serve as justification for expelling the tenant. It isn't easy to conceive of many irremediable breaches, for there have been few court cases from which a catalogue might be compiled. But if a tenant had cropped all the land to potatoes every year since the war, and thereby turned the farm into a writhing mass of eelworms, it could be argued that he had irreparably broken the covenant in his agreement " to cultivate the arable land in a proper rotation and a good and husbandlike manner."

(f) Where the tenant has gone bankrupt or compounded with his creditors.

For this to apply the tenant must either (a) have been adjudicated bankrupt by the court having jurisdiction in the area where he resides; or (b) have failed to comply with a bankruptcy notice served upon him in execution of a judgment debt; or (c) have entered into some agreement or arrangement with any three or more of his creditors in view of his insolvency.

(g) Where the tenant with whom the tenancy was made has died within three months before the date of serving the notice.

This applies to the original or direct tenant; not, for example, where the deceased had taken over the farm from an earlier tenant by means of an " assignment ".

Sometimes a farm is let to two or more tenants farming together. This is called a joint tenancy, and where it exists notice under this provision cannot be served until the last of the joint tenants dies.

The notice to quit is served on the personal representatives of the late tenant, the persons responsible for clearing up his farming and other affairs.

In addition to these deadly sins, where a farm is sublet, and the tenant is under notice to quit from his landlord and in consequence serves notice to quit on his subtenant, the latter has no right to challenge the notice served upon him.

To conclude: although the tenant has no right to turn for protection to the Agricultural Land Tribunal where he has received a notice to quit specifically on the grounds of one of the seven deadly sins, he can contest the *validity* of the stated grounds in three of the above cases, namely (b), (d) and (e). His remedy lies in an appeal to arbitration, to which end he must give the landlord notice within one month of being served with the notice to quit. Thus if the landlord, prior to serving notice to quit for failure to remedy a breach of covenant, demands that the tenant shall repair the road to the farmhouse within a fortnight, and the tenant considers that a fortnight is not nearly long enough, he may apply to an arbitrator to settle the matter.

Notice to quit part of a farm

In the ordinary course of law, a notice to quit any property must apply to the whole of it. For instance, if a house is let the landlord cannot (unless he has specially reserved the right to do so in the agreement) give the tenant notice to quit the attached conservatory; if a cottage, he cannot throw the tenant out of the garden. It must be all or nothing. This rule in general applies to farms, but section 31 of the 1948 Act lists certain cases where the landlord can give the tenant notice to quit part of the holding only. These apply to all farm tenancies which run from year to year, but of course the landlord may add to the list by agreement with the tenant.

The objects for which part of a farm may come back to the landlord are these:—
Adjustment of farm boundaries.
Building of farm cottages, or providing gardens for them.
Tree planting.
Mining, quarrying and works connected therewith.
Watercourses or reservoirs.
Making roads, railways, canals, etc.

Notice to quit part of a farm may also be given where the landlord dies and the farm is split up into a number of different ownerships.

In his notice to quit part of the holding, the landlord must say definitely that it is for this or that of the above reasons.

Within 28 days of receiving the notice, the tenant is entitled to give his landlord a written counter-notice saying that he proposes to treat the notice to quit part as a notice to treat the entire farm. If the farm extends to 1,000 acres of which the landlord needs only one rood for a farm worker's cottage, it is unlikely that the tenant will bother. It is another story if a large cut is being taken, for by enlarging the landlord's notice to extend over the whole farm there are important factors connected with compensation for disturbance (see page 43).

On giving up possession of part of his farm, the tenant is entitled to a proportionate reduction in rent. If the sum cannot be settled by the parties, an arbitrator is called in.

Earlier in this chapter we explained how a tenant can object to a notice to quit his farm. Even though notice applies to part only, he is entitled to go through the same rigmarole.

DISTURBANCE

The dictionary meaning of disturbance is " the interruption of tranquillity, peace, rest or settled condition." A farming life may have brought none of these things, so that in talking of disturbance as a cause of compensation the dictionary meaning may not wholly fit.

With a tenant farmer, disturbance refers to the agitation, flurry, bustle, and interruption of tranquillity which comes about when he ups and goes as the result of receiving noice to quit from his landlord. Of course, the same flurry may occur when he quits after himself giving notice. But, under section 34 of the 1948 Act, the right to be compensated for it only arises when the landlord gives notice to quit, for no fault on the tenant's part, and where in consequence the tenant quits.

The purpose of the compensation is to repay the tenant for losses or expenses which he unavoidably incurs in quitting the farm. The kind of items he may bring into his claim are those connected with the sale or removal of his furniture, farm implements, fixtures, live and dead farming stock, and so on.

Amount of compensation

This lies between at least one year's and at the most two year's rent of the farm. If the tenant doesn't wish to bother with the business of a detailed claim, he may settle for one year's rent. In that case he need submit no proof of having incurred any expense or loss. And " one year's rent " is at the rate he was paying for the farm at the date of quitting. That is to say, if he took it over at £200 a year but is now paying £300, then his disturbance claim will amount to £300.

But if he wishes to claim for more than a year's rent, he must do three things. He must notify his landlord in writing, not later than one month before the tenancy ends, that he proposes to claim for more than one year's rent; he must give the landlord a reasonable opportunity of valuing such goods, implements, fixtures or stock as he proposes to sell; and he must send in a detailed claim. No matter how heavy the claim, however, the landlord is not obliged to pay more than two years' rent. Any disputes go, as usual, to an arbitrator.

Where compensation is not allowed

First, it may be useful to repeat that if the tenant himself gives notice to quit he cannot claim compensation for disturbance. His departure must have been due to the landlord's action.

Even then there are several exceptions, to understand which we would ask our readers to refer back to page 38, where the seven deadly sins are considered in relation to notices to quit. We explained there that where a landlord gave a tenant notice to quit, and specified any of those acts or omissions as his reason for doing so, the tenant could not challenge the notice.

The bearing this has on disturbance is that if the landlord gave notice for any of the reasons lettered (c) to (g)—in short, bad husbandry, non-payment of rent, breach of covenant, bankruptcy or death—the tenant loses his right to claim for it.

Where part of the farm is taken

Our same section on notice to quit ended up with the landlord's right to serve notice to quit part only of a farm. On page 41 the tenant was given the right, within 28 days, to inform his landlord that he accepted the notice to quit part as notice to quit the lot.

When a tenant does quit the whole farm in those circumstances:—

(i) if the " part ", added to previous parts which may have earlier been nibbled away, is less than one-fourth of the area of the original farm, and if what remains is reasonably capable of being farmed as a separate holding, compensation for disturbance can be claimed only on the part;

(ii) but if the part, or the sum of the nibbled parts, amounts to one quarter or more, compensation will lie as above, between one and two years' rent of the whole farm.

Chapter 5

TENANT RIGHT

Every farm tenant is aware of the ingoing valuation he is required to pay on entry for assets his forerunner leaves behind, and for which correspondingly he receives compensation on quitting. It embraces a variety of things: growing crops, hay and straw, tenant's pasture, as well as "improvements" which range from buildings to unexhausted manurial values.

In the popular sense of the term these constitute tenant right, which has been defined as the interest a tenant has in the farm which he cannot take away with him but for which he is entitled to compensation at the end of his tenancy. The law, however, narrows the scope of what constitutes "tenant right matters" (which it calls "other matters"), and distinguishes them from "improvements". The reasons for this need not be laboured: in practice the tenant right valuation brings them all in. What concerns us here is first, what exactly an outgoing tenant may claim for and second, how compensation is calculated.

We have dealt with the nature of tenant's improvements in Chapter 2, but we deferred their valuation to this chapter. The outgoer's claim for improvements and tenant right is built up on the following foundations.

Old improvements

These are listed at page 16, and are improvements which were begun before 1st March, 1948. Unless some other way of valuing them is agreed between landlord and tenant, section 37 of the Agricultural Holdings Act says that the outgoer's "measure of compensation" shall be the value of the improvement to an incoming tenant. That is to say, whoever is doing the valuation looks at the building or water supply, or whatever it may be and asks himself: "What would the average tenant be prepared to pay for this, to the extent that the farm is that much better off with it?" The figure he puts it at may bear no relation to what it cost the tenant to execute: it may be a lot less, it may even be more. For instance, a rich tenant may have built a tower silo and paid a small fortune to the President of the Royal Academy for painting it so that it merged with the landscape. The average sort of farmer, while he may admit that it's pretty enough, wouldn't go so far as to offer a thousand pounds extra for its camouflage. The worth to an incoming tenant is the extent of its usefulness. Another man, on the other hand, may have had built a forthright and honest-to-God general-purpose building years ago when labour and bricks were cheap. Since then prices have risen so steeply that the building is worth more today than what it cost him. When valuing in terms of worth to an incoming tenant, the Act requires that if the landlord made any contribution towards the improvement, that factor should be taken into account.

The alternative methods of valuing an improvement depend on the mutual wishes of the parties. The most common is to write off the cost over so many years. For example, a tenant gets his landlord's written consent to construct some form of permanent sheep-dipping accommodation. They agree that its life will be about 30 years, and it costs £300, therefore its value is written down by £10 a year. If the tenant quits 11 years after, his landlord will pay him £190, being 19 years' purchase of the agreed £10 per annum.

New improvements

These are listed at page 17, and are improvements which were begun on or after 1st March, 1948. Under section 48, the measure of compensation which the outgoer can claim, if he makes his claim under the Act, is the increase in value of the farm due to the improvement. This is less obvious to apply, both in theory and practice, than the " value to an incomer " basis applying to old improvements. In effect, one considers how much the farm is worth without the improvement and how much with, and the difference represents the compensation payable. Again, if the parties prefer to adopt some other method of valuation, the Act does not hinder them.

Fourth Schedule improvements—General

We come now to the commonplace " Fourth Schedule " items that enter into more tenant right claims than not. We have refrained from listing them until now, but their detailed quotation cannot be much longer delayed. First, however, some general observations. The Fourth Schedule to the 1948 Act is divided into two parts: Part I is quite simply headed " Improvements ", Part II " Other Matters ". They have this in common: the tenant's claim does not depend on his having got advance permission, from the landlord or anyone else, to have done them, as it does with the larger-scale improvements. The measure of compensation the outgoing tenant can claim for them under section 51 of the Act is their value to an incoming tenant. Furthermore, by way as it were of a crib to assist the interpretation of that phrase, they are supported by a 10-page sixpenny pamphlet—The Agriculture (Calculation of Value for Compensation) Regulations, 1959— which gives details of how that value shall be calculated. Every Farmer, so to speak, His Own Valuer.

Where the group of improvements does differ from the other matters is that the law says they *must* be valued according to the compensation regulations. Other matters need not be, if the parties agree in writing to value them according to some preferred method.

Medium-term improvements

While the qualifying " medium-term " is not used in the Fourth Schedule, it will presently be seen that it fits all the seven improvements comprised in Part I. We have neither the room nor the right to cite all that the regulations have to say about methods of assessing them, for that would be straying from law into farm valuations. Our comments must therefore be accepted as the briefest of summaries.

1. Mole drainage and works carried out to ensure the efficient functioning thereof.

The regulations decree that where the moles discharge into a piped main drain, the outgoing tenant is compensated on a six-year basis, i.e., the reasonable net sum it cost him to mole drain, reduced by one-sixth for each year since the work was completed. Where they discharge direct into an open ditch, whether or not there are piped outfalls, the span of life is reduced to three years.

Incidentally, although the general rule is that a tenant can do any Fourth Schedule job without formal permission from anyone, if he is to claim for mole drainage he must have given the landlord at least one month's written notice of his intention to drain before starting on the work.

2. Protection of fruit trees against animals.

Compensation is based on the reasonable cost of the fencing, netting, etc., reduced where necessary according to the present condition of the fruit trees and the protection, and the further period for which it is likely to be useful.

3 and 5. Chalking and liming of land.

The value is the reasonable net cost of purchasing and applying the chalk or lime, less one-eighth for each growing season since application. Normally the outgoer will not be paid for dressings in excess of 2 tons of calcium oxide per acre—equivalent to about 4 tons of ground chalk or limestone. This rule is relaxed if he can show that more was necessary.

4. Clay burning.

It is doubtful if any farmer has voluntarily burnt clay to better his land since wages increased to five bob a week. However, if only to encourage traditional methods, compensation is based on the reasonable cost reduced by one-quarter for each season since the job was completed.

6. Application to land of purchased manure (including artificial manure).

Where no crop has been taken off, that is to say where the next occupier of the farm will receive the full benefit, the outgoer can claim the full reasonable cost of applying and spreading *purchased* fertilisers and other *purchased* manurial matter. (Home-produced manure is valued quite differently). Most manures, with the notable exception of nitrogenous artificials, are considered to benefit more than one crop, and the outgoing tenant may have a claim for the unexhausted manurial value (or " residual value ") of these. Their value is worked out according to special tables included in the regulations.

7. Consumption on the holding of corn (whether produced on the holding or not) or of cake or other feedingstuff not produced on the holding by (a) horses, cattle, sheep or pigs, or (b) poultry folded on the land as part of a system of farming practised on the holding.

This long-winded description at first reading conceals the fact that it refers to manure made by the farmer's own beasts and birds. The tenant's rights would be comparatively easy to assess if he were paid for his farmyard manure at so much a ton. The reader is asked to accept that there are reasons for preferring this round-about regulation, whereby instead he is compensated according to the residual value of the purchased food and home-grown corn fed to his animals. Their value, again, is calculated with the help of special tables included in the compensation regulations.

Tenant-right matters

The " other " matters, sometimes more descriptively called tenant-right matters, refer for the most part to crops. Although we continue to summarise their method of valuation according to the book of regulations, in all cases alternative ways may be adopted by mutual agreement.

8. Growing crops and severed or harvested crops and produce, being in either case crops or produce grown on the holding in the last year of the tenancy, but not including crops or produce which the tenant has a right to sell or remove from the holding.

9. Seeds sown and cultivations, fallows and acts of husbandry performed on the holding at the expense of the tenant.

For convenience we run these two matters together, since in practice they intermingle.

Growing crops are valued under the regulations according to what the outgoing tenant has so far put into them by the time they are taken over. This includes the cost of seeds sown, cultivations, fallows, etc., according to item 9. For instance, a crop of winter wheat at a Lady Day change of tenancy will perhaps have entailed one or two ploughings, harrowing, rolling, seeding and seed. Fertilisers, too, will be allowed, on the strength of number 6 of the medium-term improvements. In practice, the claim for purchased seeds and fertilisers should be proved by bills or receipts from the merchant. The cultivations put into a crop depend on the farmer's memory, subject to cross-questioning by the valuer acting for the other party. They are priced according to a schedule of costings prepared every year by the Central Association of Agricultural Valuers for the guidance of its members. Ploughing: between so much and so much an acre, depending on depth, type of soil, and so on. Cultivating and harrowing, rolling and seeding—all the orthodox acts of husbandry are included and priced.

Proved by bills or receipts.

Hay, straw, roots in the clamp and similar "severed or harvested crops" are valued on the basis of their "average market value on the holding during that season", i.e., their value on the farm as compared with their (higher) value in the open market; and from this a deduction is made for their manurial value, which traditionally belongs free to the land.

Farmyard manure is valued according to any labour expended in loading, carting, heaping and spreading it. Such plant food value as may be claimed for it comes under item 7 above.

It will be seen that item 8 applies only to crops and produce which the tenant has no right to sell off his farm. In most cases this means he can claim only for growing crops of cereals and of roots and fodder crops of a kind grown for feeding to his livestock. Severed crops are confined as a rule to hay, straw, roots and silage.

10. Pasture laid down with clover, grass, lucerne, sainfoin or other seeds, where either the pasture was laid down at the expense of the tenant or was paid for by the tenant on entering the holding.

This is called "tenant's pasture" to distinguish it from permanent or landlord's pasture. If it is so new that no crop has been taken from it, either by mowing or grazing, it is valued like other growing crops on the basis of seeds and labour. But once the description "maiden seeds" ceases to apply it is valued at its face value, a spot figure based on how it stands, taking into account such things as its present condition, the way it has been managed, how conveniently it is situated, how it is fenced and watered.

Not all pasture the tenant lays down may be claimed for. For example, on entering the farm the landlord may have allowed him to take over some temporary grass without paying for it, on condition that he some time ploughed up and replaced it free of charge. Again, as we explained on page 24, where an arbitrator gives a tenant consent to plough up permanent pasture, he may stipulate that on quitting he shall leave behind an equivalent area of pasture for which he shall not receive compensation.

12. Acclimatisation, hefting or settlement of hill sheep on hill land.

In jumping from 10 to 12 we have not accidentally missed out any tenant-right matter. Paragraph 11 is a general warning to the outgoing tenant that he has no right to claim for any growing or severed crops, tillages or pasture which he grew or performed contrary to his tenancy agreement. If his agreement required him, let us say, to leave one-sixth of his arable land in wheat on quitting in the spring, and in fact he sowed all of it down to wheat, he could not claim for more than the specified area. Indeed, he would be liable to a counterclaim for leaving the land out of rotation.

Item 12 applies to those hill farms where it is customary for an incoming tenant to take over the sheep flock. Such flocks are described as being bound to the land, and by being for generations born on the spot they acquire a sense of where they belong—very useful on a fell farm which may stretch for miles without fences—and an immunity to tick-borne diseases. On any particular farm, such acclimatised sheep are more valuable than otherwise comparable strangers, and it has long been recognised that this extra value is measurable in terms of cash. The regulations give the outgoer the right to claim for this extra value, which is based on a maximum of 15s. a head or 15 per cent of the market value of the sheep, whichever is the less.

The word "hefting", by the way, means the herding of the flock until it gets acclimatised to the confines of its home grounds; in Wales the process is called "settlement".

HIGH FARMING

In all but a fractional minority of cases, the tenant-right valuation affords the outgoer at least adequate compensation for the legacy of improvements and other matters he bequeathes to his successor. Occasionally, however, you come across a paragon who has so bravely and consistently improved the farm that the sum total of the items in his valuation falls short of the amount by which the farm has gained in value through his management. Virtue then brings its cash reward.

Section 56 of the Agricultural Holdings Act, 1948, provides that where a tenant has increased the general value of his farm by the continuous adoption of a special system more beneficial than the farming system laid down in his tenancy agreement—or, if there is no agreement, more beneficial than the system normally practised on farms such as his—he can claim compensation for the increase. Two qualifications attach to this right. He must have had a record made of the state of the farm at the time he began to improve it, in order that whoever assesses the value may make a before and after comparison. And he must notify his landlord, at least one month before the tenancy ends, that he means to make such a claim.

The measure of compensation is the increased value of the holding attributable to his special policy of farming—and remarkably difficult it is to translate into £ s. d.

MARKET GARDENS

In the law's eyes a Market Garden is an " agricultural holding ", only rather more so. All we have expounded about landlord and tenant in previous chapters, and will conclude in the next, applies to market garden as well as farm tenancies. In addition, the quitting tenant may claim, over and above his claim for improvements and tenant-right, compensation for five specialised items.

Before considering the nature of a market garden, we might list these five special improvements. They are found in the Fifth Schedule to the Agricultural Holdings Act, 1948.

1. Planting of standard or other fruit trees permanently set out.
2. Planting of fruit bushes permanently set out.
3. Planting of strawberry plants.
4. Planting of asparagus, rhubarb and other vegetable crops which continue productive for two or more years.
5. Erection, alteration or enlargement of buildings for the purpose of the trade or business of a market gardener.

The outgoing market gardener's claim to compensation does not depend on getting prior consent from his landlord for any of these things. He can plant the specified plants in the specified way and

erect, alter or enlarge his specialised buildings as the spirit and the
market move him. A warning might be inserted about fruit trees
and bushes *not* permanently set out, e.g., in a nursery. For these
the tenant has no claim. His remedy is to remove them, at any
time before his tenancy ends. If not, they pass free to the landlord,
and an attempt to whip them away after the tenancy ends may
make the tenant liable to his landlord for damages.

Unless the parties choose to agree on some other " fair and
reasonable " compensation, market garden improvements are
valued on the basis of their worth to an incoming tenant. Alternatively they may agree that the Evesham Custom shall apply to the
holding, a provision shortly to be explained.

What is a Market Garden ?

Sections 67–69 of the Act, which cover the subject, do not
define " market garden ". Its ancestor, the Agricultural Holdings
Act, 1923, at least made an attempt, by calling it " a holding
cultivated wholly or mainly for the purpose of the trade or business
of market gardening ". As a first step towards the light few would
condemn that as beyond contempt; the clay feet showed themselves when one discovered no complementary description of
" market gardening ". It was left to the learned judge, in the case
of *Watters v. Hunter,* 1927, to fill the gap. It meant " the trade
or business which produces a class of goods characteristic of a
greengrocer's shop, and which in the ordinary course reaches that
shop via the early morning market, where such goods are disposed
of wholesale. It is no doubt the case that this class of goods
includes small fruit and, it may be, flowers."

Such a description cannot be far removed from the market gardener's own conception of his trade. A tenant may, however,
smother his whole farm with strawberries, asparagus, rhubarb and
other Fifth Schedule delights without having the right to a penn'orth
of outgoing for them. A market garden in fact may not be a
market garden under the Act.

There are two principal ways in which it qualifies for legal
recognition. (Yet a third figures in the Act, but it is by now more
of historical than practical importance, so we shall leave it out.)
The simplest is where the landlord says in writing " I agree that
Cloche Farm shall be treated as a market garden." But not all
landlords care to commit themselves by this procedure to a possibly
astronomical bill for compensation at some time in the future.
Indeed, a standard sort of clause in tenancy agreements runs:
" Neither the farm nor any part thereof shall be deemed to be let
as a market garden."

This is where the determined market gardener has a second
string. If the landlord refuses to agree that a farm, or some part

of it, shall be treated as a market garden—or if, while not positively refusing, he fails to agree to the tenant's request within a reasonable time—the tenant may ask the Agricultural Land Tribunal to direct that it shall be so treated. As with all applications to them, the Tribunal must hear both sides of the case, and before saying yes they must be satisfied that the farm or part is suitable for market gardening.

Where the Tribunal do give the direction applied for, the tenant will have the same rights—the greatest being the right to make Fifth Schedule improvements—as if he had got the landlord's own consent. But come what may, his rights to compensation for them will be based on the Evesham Custom.

The Evesham Custom

Nobody who knows what put the Vale of Evesham on the map will need to inquire why the custom is so called. It operates thus: where the tenancy of a market garden comes to an end through the tenant himself giving notice to quit or going bankrupt, the outgoer cannot claim compensation for the special market garden improvements unless he can find a " substantial and otherwise suitable person " who is willing to take a new tenancy, on the same terms as the existing one, and who will pay him all the compensation due to him as an outgoer.

It will be noticed that this obligation applies only when the tenant quits through his own act or suffers financial misfortune. If he departs as the result of notice from his landlord, he has no need to scrub round his friends and relations in search of a successor. Again, said successor will be obliged to settle *all* the compensation due to the outgoer, not merely his claim for the special improvements.

The tenant has one month, from the date of his giving notice or going bankrupt, in which to produce a written offer from a suitable tenant, but if the landlord agrees the time limit may be extended. For his part, the landlord has three months from the date the offer is produced in which to say yes or no. If he fails, or unreasonably refuses, to accept the nominee within that time, he himself becomes liable to pay the tenant his market garden and other compensation. If he maintains that the fellow is neither " substantial " nor " otherwise suitable ", the position is less clear, though clearly more delicate, and best left for an arbitrator to decide.

Should a tenant be unable to produce a willing successor, he loses his rights to Fifth Schedule improvements. But this does not affect his other rights for compensation as applicable to an ordinary farm tenancy.

Chapter 6

COUNTERCLAIMS AND SETTLEMENT

In our many references to goings-on at the end of a tenancy, and to claims which arise when a farm tenant quits, we may have given the impression that the fortunate fellow is exclusively at the receiving end. We now proceed to pierce that illusion.

We have seen that every tenant-farmer is under certain obligations to farm reasonably well. The general law requires it, even though he has not promised in writing to be a good husbandman. Any tenancy agreement he may have signed will most certainly put specific obligations upon him, not only to do a share of the repairs but to order his cropping so that he does not impoverish the soil.

At the end of the tenancy there are usually some flies to be extracted from the ointment, and where the tenant has fallen short of his liabilities the landlord may require him to pay the cost of putting things right, by means of a claim for dilapidations and deterioration. The difference between the two terms is that dilapidations refer to particular items needing to be put right—broken windows, dead hedges, etc.—while deterioration applies to a general state of run-downness.

The claim for dilapidations may be made either under the terms of the tenancy agreement, or through the right given by section 57 of the Agricultural Holdings Act, 1948. The landlord may choose which of the two authorities he prefers, but he must claim wholly under either one or the other.

Compensation under the Act is based on the cost of making good the damage done: so many yards of road to be repaired at so much a square yard, for example. There is no statutory list of what may or may not go into a dilapidations claim, but valuers tend to think of them under four headings:—

(1) Houses, cottages and buildings.

(2) Fences, gates, roads, ditches and drains.

(3) Foul land and irregularity of cropping.

(4) Produce sold off.

The extent of the tenant's liability to repair the "fixed equipment" comprised in the first two groups depends either on what he covenanted to do in his tenancy agreement, or what the Repairs Regulations say. These things were the subject of Chapter 2.

Foul land connotes land which is inexcusably dirty, neglected and hungry: no valuer minds only a few weeds. The landlord bases his claim on the estimated cost of bringing back each foul field into tolerable heart: so many cultivations, so much fertiliser

So many yards of road to be repaired at so much per square yard.

and lime. As to irregular cropping, it will be recalled that where a tenant is required to cultivate the arable land according to a specified rotation, he may nevertheless go his own way during the tenancy, provided he leaves the farm in that rotation. If he does not, the landlord's claim is calculated according to the cost of bringing the fields into order, including such items as cultivations for making up the tilth and the replacement of manurial losses.

The last heading is a warning to the outgoing farmer not to sell off any hay, straw, roots or manure produced during his last year. If he does, he will be dilapidated at a figure representing the difference between the cost of replacing the stuff from outside and the compensation he would have got for it had it remained on the farm to form part of his tenant-right claim.

General deterioration

The last section of the previous chapter gave the outgoing tenant the right to claim for high farming, where he had generally improved the holding by continuously farming in a manner at once the admiration and envy of his neighbours. The other side of the coin allows the landlord to claim for, as it were, low farming. Where a tenant has let down the holding so consistently according to the rules of bad husbandry that the sum total of specific dilapidations charged against him inadequately covers the harm done, the landlord may make an additional claim for general deterioration. He must give the tenant notice of his intention to claim at least one month before the tenancy finishes, and his claim is based on the decreased value of the farm due to the tenant's abominations.

SETTLEMENT OF CLAIMS

It will have become apparent to the conscientious reader that when a tenancy comes to an end the tenant may have several different claims to make against his landlord: certainly for tenant-right and improvements, possibly for disturbance, fixtures and high farming. On his side the landlord may have reason to counter-claim against the tenant for dilapidations and deterioration.

Each of these claims is the subject of written notices which the parties must serve on each other as a necessary formality.* Where specific time-limits apply we have already mentioned them in their separate context. Beyond these, section 70 lays down an important general rule: to establish the right to these end-of-tenancy claims, the tenant must notify the landlord in writing (and the other way about) of his *intention* to claim for such-and-such not later than two months after the tenancy has expired.

Such a notice is a mere preliminary, for it need include no details of amounts involved: it suffices merely to state the nature of the claim and upon what authority it is made. For instance, a tenant who quit as the result of notice from his landlord might inform him merely: " I hereby give you notice that I intend to make against you a claim for disturbance under section 34 of the Agricultural Holdings Act, 1948." Landlord to tenant: " I hereby give you notice of my intention to claim for dilapidations under clause 23 of our tenancy agreement dated 29th September, 1938."

When it comes to settling the details of claims and counter-claims there are further specific time limits. Basically, the landlord and the tenant are given four months from the day the tenancy ended to agree upon them amicably. If they (or more probably the valuers acting for them) have not by then finished arguing, either party may apply to the Minister of Agriculture for a two months' extension. And again, before the six months are up, a second application may be made to the Minister, extending the time to a total of eight months from the end of the tenancy.

If by the end of those four, six or eight months the parties have not agreed on the fair compensation for all or any of their claims, the only way the disputed ones may be enforced is by submitting

---

* A notice may be served in one of three ways: (1) by delivering it personally to the one concerned; (2) by leaving it at his last known address; (3) by sending it to him by registered letter or recorded delivery.

them to arbitration. Yet again there is an element of despatch, for an arbitrator must be appointed by agreement (or, if the contending parties cannot agree even on that, an application must be made to the Minister to appoint one) within one month after the end of the four-, six- or eight-month limit for amicable settlement.

The parties, incidentally, are not compelled to wait as long as four months before resorting to arbitration. It may take them or their valuers but half a day to conclude that nothing is likely to alter the other chap's highflown (or lowflown) ideas of what constitutes value. In such event they may hasten to arbitration straight away.

Once the sums for compensation have been agreed—or, in the case of arbitration, " awarded "—they must be paid within 14 days of becoming due. Otherwise they are treated as a civil debt, recoverable through the County Court.

ARBITRATION

As we have often had occasion to refer to arbitration, we conclude this part of our book with an outline of what it entails.

Arbitration is a way of settling disputes between two or more people without, in the popular phrase, " going to law about it." Instead of appearing before a judge, the parties refer their troubles to an arbitrator. The proceedings are on the whole far less formal, less ceremonial.

Nevertheless, although the hearing may take place in the near-festive atmosphere of the Traveller's Rest, and everybody knew the arbitrator when he was but a sprightly lad booking the sales at the Wednesday cattle market, and the expert witnesses don't mind being questioned as long as they can slip out in time for the three-fifteen milking, an arbitration is a serious matter. The arbitrator has in many ways the same powers as a judge, and his "judgment", called an " award ", cannot be challenged on matters of fact.

Arbitration, as an alternative to action at law, comes into many aspects of trade and business. Applied to disputes between landlords and tenants of farms, it is subject to special rules, set out in the Sixth Schedule to the 1948 Act.

The vast bulk of such disagreements which defy clearing up by mutual give and take cannot legally be settled other than by arbitration. For many years the agricultural law-makers have insisted on this. The exceptions which allow a resort to the law courts are too rarefied even to mention.

In fact, arbitration has many advantages over an action at law. The arbitrator is usually a specialist on the technical points in dispute, whereas a judge—who is concerned with their legal rather than their factual side—may, with all respect, scarcely know hay from straw, a blackface from whiteheads, or the current market value of anything. Again, the various phases of the proceedings are subject to pretty short time limits, which make mockery of the law's delays. Geographically, too, those concerned in an arbitration in, say, south-west Cornwall can more conveniently assemble in Lands End than in Lincoln's Inn.

Who may arbitrate

You or I, Squire Western, Uncle Tom Cobleigh, almost anyone may be appointed arbitrator, as long as he has no vested interest in the matter disputed and is independent of the parties. Arbitrators over farming matters are naturally best dealt with by those who know something about farming: usually a surveyor, land agent or auctioneer in rural practice.

The choice is generally made by agreement between the landlord and tenant or the valuers acting for them. One or other may submit a list of three or four names out of which the other chooses him, him or him. To avoid disappointment they may first telephone the selected man to ask if he will be willing to act; if the answer is yes, they both sign and submit a formal appointment.

Sometimes there is a deadlock. No matter how many names each party suggests, the other finds fault. In that event an application, with a fee of £1, is made to the Minister of Agriculture to select an arbitrator. In practice, the application is sent to the Ministry of Agriculture, Fisheries and Food, Great Westminster House, Horseferry Road, London, S.W.1. There they keep a record of suitable persons who are willing to be called on, and after making certain enquiries Mr. A. B. is formally notified of his appointment.

From the day of his appointment the arbitrator has six weeks in which to get the whole affair settled. The Minister, however, does have powers to extend the period.

Statement of case

As a preliminary also subject to time limits, the parties must within 14 days send the arbitrator a statement of their respective cases, including all particulars that will clarify the matter. The object of this is to tell the arbitrator exactly what claims each is making, and possibly the legal grounds they are based on. Assuming, for instance, that the arbitration is to do with the rent of a farm, the landlord's statement would give a brief description of the place, the acreage, the present rent, how long the tenant has been in occupation, and any other background information likely to be helpful. He might then say that in his opinion the farm is worth £400 a year, and add a few statements in support. He need disclose no evidence yet: that will be called upon during the hearing.

The tenant's case will be represented in a similar manner, except that for such and such reasons he claims that the rent should be £250, and will support this by reference to the terms of his agreement, the carrying capacity of the farm in terms of crops and stock, the capital he has put into it, and so forth.

A wholly commendable effect of these statements of case is that they cut out a great deal of side-issue time wasting. Any later amendments may be made only with the arbitrator's consent; at the hearing the parties must stick within the limits imposed in this way on themselves.

The hearing

The date, time and place of the hearing are at the arbitrator's discretion. As a matter of common politeness he will offer a choice of two or three; he may later make changes if one or another party produces good reasons. But once the rendezvous is fixed, if through sheer obstinacy one of the parties refuses to attend, the arbitrator may proceed without him.

There are no laws controlling the order of speaking at the hearing, but the usual procedure is this:—

The party making the disputed claim (the " claimant ") starts the ball rolling. He may do this in person, or through a valuer, surveyor, solicitor, even a barrister.

He then calls his witnesses, who are examined by himself (or his advocate), cross-examined by the other side, and re-examined by himself.

The other party (the " respondent ") has his say.

The respondent's witnesses are correspondingly examined, cross-examined and re-examined.

The respondent sums up his case.

The claimant replies.

Then, when the arbitrator is satisfied that all have said their say, he formally closes the case, and sets about his main task. Usually he will need to visit the farm which harbours the dispute. Some arbitrators insist on going alone; if either party wishes to accompany him, the other must be invited too.

The award

The arbitrator's decision emerges in official sort of wording, in which he " awards and determines " that one party is entitled to receive from the other such a sum in respect of his claim or claims. He notifies both parties when it is ready, and that it can be taken up on payment of the costs involved.

PART II

THE FARMER AND WHITEHALL

Whitehall, a straight and not unimpressive street in Westminster, to many minds is no more than another word for " them "—the government, the civil service, the Man from the Ministry. In this part we consider several ways in which the farmer's interests are safeguarded, controlled, restricted, shalt and shalt-notted and otherwise affected by the central government, the State.

Chapter 7

GUARANTEED PRICES

Guaranteed prices and assured markets: this is the heading of Part I of the Agriculture Act, 1947, whose avowed object is to promote and maintain a stable and efficient agricultural industry. The intervening years have brought some amendments, but more in detail than in principle, and the 1947 Act remains the source from which the annual price reviewers take their authority.

Twelve products are the subject of price and market control. They fall into two groups:—

Crops: wheat, barley, oats, rye, potatoes and sugar beet.

Livestock and livestock products: fat cattle, fat sheep, fat pigs, cow's milk (liquid), eggs (hen and duck in shell) and wool.

The Minister of Agriculture has powers to add to the list.

At least once a year the Minister is required to hold a review of the general state of agriculture. This is the familiar Annual Price Review, where officials of the Ministry get together with " such bodies of persons as appear to them to represent the interests of producers in the agricultural industry "—in practice represented by

So much for the annual review.

the National Farmers' Union—and chew both the fat and the lean. Not only do they discuss prices; the law requires that the agenda

63

FGL   5 shall include the general economic conditions then reigning and the future prospects of the farming industry.

So much for the compulsory annual review. There are also provisions for special reviews. If in the Minister's opinion unpredictable things have happened between annual reviews so as, for instance, to have caused a substantial rise in farming costs, he may hold a special review without waiting for next February or March.

The guaranteed prices settled at the annual review apply, generally speaking, for the next 12 months or so. With crops they apply to the coming harvest.

To encourage a measure of stability in the industry generally, and to avoid severe fluctuations in farmers' incomes, the Agriculture Act, 1957, provides certain long-term assurances. These operate in two ways: firstly in connection with individual products, and secondly with regard to guaranteed prices as a whole.

First, this year's price for *any* individual product, whether crop or livestock, must not fall below 96 per cent of last year's. Furthermore, if the price of any *livestock or livestock produce* is reduced, the reduction must not exceed a total of 9 per cent in any period of three years. An example or two will clarify these principles.

After the price review for 1961, the guaranteed price for wheat harvested that year was 26s. 11d. per cwt. In 1962 it would not have been allowed to fall below 96 per cent of 26s. 11d. That is to say, the lowest the wheat grower need have anticipated was 25s. 10d.

Again, the 1961–62 price for guaranteed fat cattle was 167s. per live cwt. For 1962–63 it could not have been lower than 96 per cent of 167s., namely 160s. 4d. Furthermore, being one of the group of livestock and livestock products, on the longer term "nine per cent" issue it cannot, in 1964–65, be less than 91 per cent of 167s., namely 162s. per live cwt.

The second overall safeguard works in a rather different way, but without prejudice to the above prices for *individual* products. It takes into account not only the subsidies and deficiency payments by which guaranteed prices are kept bolstered up to their higher than free market level, but also some of the numerous " production grants " available to the farmer. These grants fall broadly into two classes. Some are associated more with farm ownership, notably the Farm Improvements Scheme, others with farm occupation, e.g., the fertiliser and lime subsidies, grants for ploughing and drainage, calf and hill cattle subsidies and so on. For our purposes it is the latter class, the so-called " relevant " production grants, that count. What this overall long-term assurance boils down to is that in any year the *total* value of the guaranteed prices and relevant production grants shall be maintained at not less than 97½ per cent of their value in the preceding year, after allowing for certain changes in costs.

How price guarantees operate

To give working effect to the decisions made at each annual review, the Minister of Agriculture makes what are called Guarantee Orders. They are of two kinds.

One kind provides that he shall pay to the appropriate marketing boards sums of money representing the difference between (a) the value of produce sold by a board on the basis of its guaranteed price and (b) the actual receipts of the board from the sale of the produce.

The other allows the Minister to pay sums of money direct to the producers (or other persons or bodies) based on the difference between (a) the guaranteed price and (b) the prices, estimated or ascertained, actually received by them.

Guarantee orders may also provide that the Minister or marketing boards shall buy produce at guaranteed prices, and that the Minister shall repay the boards their trading losses.

In present-day fact, the guarantees for milk, eggs, potatoes and wool are implemented through their respective marketing boards (whose functions are outlined in Chapter 9); the sugar beet guarantee is implemented through the British Sugar Corporation, while cereal and fatstock are the subject of deficiency payments administered by the Minister of Agriculture; all in the following manner.

Fatstock

Under the fatstock guarantee scheme, individual producers may claim a subsidy on fat cattle (steers and heifers, sheep and pigs) which they have sold and which—on the authority of an approved market, slaughterhouse or bacon factory—have been certified as eligible because they measure up to the required standards of weight and quality.

For cattle and sheep there is a seasonal scale of weekly standard prices, which ties up with the current year's guaranteed prices. Each week the rate at which the guarantee payment is made has to be newly calculated. To this end the latest available four weeks' actual market prices are added to the estimated market prices for the coming four weeks, and divided by eight. This eight-week average is compared with the seasonal scale price for the week, and the amount by which it falls short, if any, represents that week's guaranteed payment.

With fat pigs the approach is different, for they have no seasonal scale as a yardstick. Instead they are linked up with a standard feed ration. As the cost of that ration goes up or down, so does the subsidy. In any one week the average price of pigs is calculated on the same basis as are cattle and sheep: that is to say, four weeks' actual and four weeks' estimated prices. The average price is compared with the price of the standard ration, and the amount of any shortfall is paid to the farmer by way of guarantee.

Milk

The price guarantee for milk is operated through the Milk Marketing Boards, who are the first buyers of all milk except that sold by producer-retailers, for whom there are special arrangements. The Government controls the maximum retail prices for milk and the various distributive margins and allowances. The Board must adjust their first-hand selling price to allow for the appropriate margin to the trade. Milk in excess of liquid requirements is manufactured into dairy products, and realises a lower price.

The guarantee price is determined at the Annual Review and applies to what is known as the standard quantity. The standard quantity varies from year to year; it represents the previous years' sales for liquid consumption, plus a necessary reserve to ensure adequate supplies throughout the year. The Board's receipts from the sale of all milk are pooled and, except for small regional differentials, each producer receives the same basic price for milk of T.T. standard. At the beginning of the " milk year " the M.M.B. announce provisional monthly prices for the ensuing 12-month period, based on the guaranteed price and their estimate of future production. The difference between what the Board make out of their milk sales and what the guarantee entitles them to receive is made good by the Government. When the Board make more money from their sales than their entitlement under the guarantee, they are required to make a repayment to the Government.

Eggs

Like the M.M.B., the British Egg Marketing Board have full trading powers. All egg producers may register with the Board, while those with more than 50 hens must register. The guarantee is payable on eggs passing through packing stations, the eggs being stamped with the familiar lion to show that they have received subsidy. At the Annual Review a price is guaranteed to the Board for shell eggs for the ensuing year. To arrive at the Government's financial commitment, an estimated selling price is agreed, based on twice the current year's actual selling price plus the price from the previous year, the total being divided by three.

Any gap between the review price and this estimated price is bridged by a flat rate of subsidy per dozen eggs, payable to the Board. The level of the estimated market price affects not only the flat rate of subsidy, but also the operation of the profit and loss sharing arrangement.

Through this arrangement, if the Board's actual selling price exceeds the estimated price, the excess is shared between the Board and the Government in the ratio of three-to-one. The Board must place 40 per cent of their share in a reserve fund and distribute the remainder to producers. If, on the other hand, the Board's actual selling price falls short of the estimated price, 40 per cent of the loss is borne by the Board and 60 per cent by the Government. But the Board bear only 10 per cent of any loss in excess of 6d. per dozen.

There is yet another complication to these workings, for the guarantee is linked to the rise and fall in the price of a standard poultry feed ration. Adjustments are made to the guaranteed prices at four-weekly intervals throughout the year by means of a formula which automatically takes account of feed costs.

The Board prescribe minimum prices to be paid to producers for first quality eggs sold through packing stations, and under the marketing scheme the packers act as agents of the Board.

Slight differences distinguish the guarantee arrangements for duck eggs, but it comes to much the same in the end.

Wool

The guarantee for fleece wool, i.e., wool shorn from live sheep, works through the Wool Marketing Board. The Board receive a fixed price for every pound of fleece wool bought from producers. The wool is sold at auction, and if it makes less than the guaranteed price the balance is made up from a " price stabilisation fund ", which is primarily fed from the profits made during the fat years. If the lean years predominate and exhaust the kitty, the Exchequer steps in with a sweetener. Payment to producers is made by wool merchants acting under contract on the Board's behalf.

Cereals

The guarantees for wheat, barley, oats and rye are administered by the Ministry of Agriculture by means of deficiency payments. Where the national average price falls short of the guaranteed price, the difference is made up by a cheque to each producer. Wheat guaranteed prices are varied according to the season, to discourage a rush of marketing at harvest time and encourage a more orderly spread of deliveries to merchants. The others operate at a fixed price throughout the whole " cereal year ".

Payments for wheat and rye are based on the quantity of millable grain sold and delivered to an authorised merchant and for which he issues an approving certificate. Barley, oats and mixed corn have to be treated differently, since so much of them is grown not for sale but for home feeding. In their case payment is on an acreage basis: so much per acre of grain grown for harvesting, the calculation of which combines the price deficiency per cwt. multiplied by the year's average yield of merchantable grain throughout the United Kingdom.

Potatoes

Unlike the other boards mentioned above, the Potato Marketing Board do not possess full selling powers. They have powers to control marketing but, subject to meeting the Board's regulations, producers may sell their potatoes to whom they wish. Producers of one acre or more who wish to sell any part of their crop must, however, register with the Board and pay an annual contribution towards their operating costs.

The guarantee is in the form of a deficiency payment made in any season in which the average market price received by growers for potatoes sold for human consumption (other than new potatoes) falls below the guaranteed price for that season. The average price is calculated from returns made by merchants and grower-salesmen. The deficiency payment is made not to the individual grower but to the Board, and the Board may spend it, for the benefit of the industry, as they think fit.

Sugar beet

Sugar beet is grown under contracts which are made every year between farmers and the British Sugar Corporation. The acreage for which the Corporation may contract is determined from year to year during the price review, as is the price, based on sugar content. In their turn, the Corporation negotiate with the refiners on the basis of world prices for sugar. If their dealings reflect a loss, it is made up by a levy on all sugar and molasses, home-grown or imported, entering the United Kingdom market.

Chapter 8

COMMITTEES AND TRIBUNALS

That same Agriculture Act of 1947 which provided much of the material for our last chapter set up two sorts of bodies whose titles are known to every farmer. In an age when so much and so many are known by initials, it will suffice to say that we refer to the C.A.E.C. and the A.L.T.

COUNTY AGRICULTURAL EXECUTIVE COMMITTEES

These were established for "promoting agricultural development and efficiency by such means as the Minister may direct" and for exercising various other functions which he had, and still has, power to delegate.

A Committee exists in each administrative county, except London, and consists of not more than 12 members.

Five of the 12 are appointed by the Minister direct. One of them must be a member of the County Council, and he is appointed after consultation with the council. The idea behind this is to link up the work of the C.A.E.C. with the agricultural duties—mainly education and the provision of smallholdings—of the County Council. The other four people directly appointed are typically those with special qualifications or experience appropriate to the local type of farming.

The remaining seven are called "nominated" members. Three of them represent farmers, two landowners and two agricultural workers. They, too, are "appointed" by the Minister, although not chosen by him. In practice the three farmers are put up for nomination by the National Farmers' Union, the two landowners by the Country Landowners' Association and the two workers by the National Union of Agricultural Workers.

The chairman and deputy chairman of a C.A.E.C. are both designated by the Minister. Members of the Committee have a three-year term of office and are then eligible for reappointment. In certain circumstances—ranging from bankruptcy to infirmity of mind—a member may be ousted and replaced before his term is up.

Besides being and acting themselves, a C.A.E.C. may (with the Minister's approval) and must (if he so requires) appoint subcommittees and district committees and delegate functions to them.

In general the C.A.E.C.s act as agents for the Minister. In many cases where the Agriculture Acts say that such and such shall be referred to the Minister, in practice the C.A.E.C. is meant.

"Many cases" in these days approximates to an overstatement. For the first eleven years of its life the 1947 Act contained active provisions for ensuring that farmers behaved according to the rules of good husbandry, and that landowners managed their land according to the rules of good estate management. If they did not, they could be put under official supervision, served with directions stating specifically which socks they must pull up, and as a last resort dismissed from their land. The Agriculture Act, 1958, did away with all that and so deprived the C.A.E.C.s of an important

As a last resort dismissed from their land.

function. It further transferred other functions to other authorities, leaving the Committees stripped of all but their underwear.

At the time many thought that it would have been kinder to disband the C.A.E.C.s altogether. However, the then Minister of Agriculture assured the House of Commons that they had yet a part to play. Their task thenceforth would be to promote the general development of farming in their respective counties, where their wide knowledge of local conditions would assist Whitehall in working out agricultural policy and technical development.

So today, although a very few of the functions which gave the Committees substance and prestige still are vested in them, their duties are general rather than specific. In effect, where once they laid their shoulders to the wheel they now keep an ear on the ground.

AGRICULTURAL LAND TRIBUNALS

Throughout the first part of this book we at times, though reluctantly, disclosed the fact that landlords and tenants do not always see eye to eye. Indeed, we gave many examples of possible bones of contention. Run of the mill disagreements, we showed, where they cannot be amicably resolved can be legally settled only by going to arbitration. A fair crop of bones, on the other hand, needs to be referred to higher authority. This is where the Agricultural Land Tribunals start to function.

There are eight such tribunals in England and Wales, each responsible for an area comprising a group of administrative counties. In the north, for example, the counties of Cumberland, Westmorland, Northumberland and Durham constitute the Northern Province and are served from Newcastle-on-Tyne. The three Ridings make up the Yorkshire Province, with its own tribunal; another tribunal serves Wales as a whole.

Each A.L.T. basically consists of three members. The key man is the chairman. He must be a barrister or solicitor of not less than seven years' standing. He is appointed by the Lord Chancellor; he holds office for three years, at the end of which he may be reappointed. For each tribunal the Lord Chancellor keeps an up-to-date panel of deputy chairmen, who likewise must be barristers or solicitors of seven years' standing. Similarly he draws up a list of persons representing farming and landowning interests respectively. Suitable names for this panel are suggested from time to time by the National Farmers' Union and the Country Landowners' Association.

The tribunal in action consists of three members: the chairman, one from the panel of farmers, one from the panel of landowners. If the chairman thinks it needful he may add two " assessors ", whom he chooses from a panel of persons nominated by the President of the Royal Institution of Chartered Surveyors.

From this it will appear that, although it may properly be called *the* tribunal, the personnel alter from one case (" hearing " or " reference ") to the next. Only the chairman remains constant; and if he cannot attend even his place may be taken by a deputy chairman or the chairman of another tribunal.

What may go before the A.L.T.

Tribunals are limited in the kinds of dispute that come within their orbit. Most of these we have brought into Part I of this book, but since such references occur as-and-when, it may assist readers who fancy the idea of calling upon them to gather together the list of permissible applications, prior to saying a word about procedure.

For a start, applications must be worded substantially on the

lines of the appropriate forms.* These forms are numbered from
1 to 14, and all but Nos. 3, 4, 13 and 14, have a complementary
form, numbered 1R, 2R, etc., on the lines of which the other party
sets out his reply. We will omit the Reply forms and confine
ourselves to the applications.

Form 1. Application for consent to operation of notice to quit.
The story behind this is told at page 35 of this book.

Form 2. Application for certificate of bad husbandry.
See page 39.

*Form 3. Application for variation or revocation of condition
imposed by the Tribunal.*
On page 37 it was said that where the tribunal give their
approval of a landlord's notice to quit, they may impose conditions to ensure that he uses the farm for the reason his notice
to quit was allowed to proceed. There may be cases where a
change of circumstances makes it impracticable for the landlord
subsequently to abide by those conditions. In such event he may
apply, on Form 3, for the tribunal to change their minds.

Form 4. Application for penalty for breach of condition.
Again, this ties up with the tribunal's consent to a notice to
quit. It was added, on page 37, that where the tribunal consented
to notice to quit on certain conditions, and the landlord did not
comply with them, they could penalise him to a maximum of two
years' rent. Action in such cases is taken by the Treasury Solicitor,
who "hereby applies" on Form 4.

Form 5. Application for direction to provide fixed equipment.
This is used by a tenant with page 18 of this book in mind.

Form 6. Application for approval of long-term improvement.

*Form 7. Application for determination that landlord has failed
to carry out improvements within a reasonable time.*
The purpose of both these forms is revealed at page 17.

*Form 8. Application for direction to treat an agricultural holding
as a market garden.*
See page 53.

*Form 9. Application for direction to avoid or relax covenant
against the burning of heather or grass.*
A tenancy agreement may contain a clause which prohibits the

---

* The official forms, and the rules of procedure, are contained in The
Agricultural Land Tribunals and Notices to Quit Order, 1959 (S.I. 1959
No. 81), The Agricultural Land Tribunals (Amendment) Order, 1959
(S.I. 1959 No. 359) and The Agricultural Land Tribunals (Amendment)
Order, 1961 (S.I. 1961 No. 1755).

tenant from burning off heather or grass. If the tenant considers that this ban is preventing his proper farming of the land, and the landlord refuses to see his point of view, he may request the tribunal to override the provision.

Form 10. Application for determination that a person be treated as owner of land.
This is a somewhat complicated matter to do with the ownership of ironstone land, and need not be pursued.

Form 11. Application to postpone operation of notice to quit.
The circumstances which give rise to this application are noted on page 38.

Form 12. Application under Land Drainage Act, 1961.

Form 13. Notice by applicant under Rule 18a (4) of the Agricultural Land Tribunals Rules, 1959.

Form 14. Application for variation of Order made under Land Drainage Act, 1961.
The purpose of these forms is explained in Chapter 21.

How applications are made and heard

The application forms listed in the paragraphs above are obtainable from the secretaries of the several Agricultural Land Tribunals to whom, after being duly completed and signed, they are sent back. At least two copies must be submitted: more if more than one landlord and one tenant are concerned in the dispute; and it is usually necessary to add plans and other documents pertaining to the farm. The secretary then serves a set of the papers on the other party who, if he intends to oppose the application in whole or in part, has a month in which to submit his Reply form.

After this the tribunal fix a date, time and place for the hearing, which normally must not be less than a fortnight ahead. Unless for exceptional reasons, the tribunal function in public. The parties concerned, and their counsel, solicitors and other representatives all have the right to be heard. The applicant is given the first hearing; after that the tribunal can dictate the order of appearance. Evidence may be spoken or written, and everyone concerned may be examined, re-examined and cross-examined as in an arbitration or court of law. The tribunal may at any time visit the farm out of which the proceedings arise, or any other holdings owned or occupied by the parties, so that the members can satisfy themselves by a good look round.

The tribunal's decision, which may be a majority one if all its members are not of one mind, is delivered in writing, and must be backed by a statement explaining its reasons. The secretary then sends copies to all the parties concerned.

If at any time difficulties arise over points of law, either party may request the tribunal to refer the question to the High Court for a ruling by a judge.

The costs of a hearing before the tribunal are normally shared by the parties concerned, but where one of them appears to have acted out of sheer cussedness—where, in official terms, he has acted " frivously, vexatiously or oppressively "—in applying for or in connection with the matter, the tribunal may order him to pay most or all of the expenses involved, including the other man's costs.

The parties' rights to question the tribunal's wisdom are limited only to questions of law. There is no appeal against their decision on points of fact.

Chapter 9

AGRICULTURAL MARKETING BOARDS

The main object of a marketing scheme is to induce farmers who produce such and such a product to co-operate in selling it. The procedure for getting a scheme going is the same in all cases; but the powers and duties of each individual marketing board which comes about where the procedure is successful are variable. So we have one consolidating Act—the Agricultural Marketing Act, 1958—dealing with general procedure, and a string of other legislation, such as the Milk Marketing Scheme (Approval) Order, 1933, dealing with specific products.

Marketing schemes in general

The workings and requirements of the Agricultural Marketing Act are easiest to grasp if we take a fictitious example. Let us assume the product is celery.

The first step towards creating a board is for a number of celery growers to get together and concoct a scheme for regulating the marketing of celery within a certain area, e.g., England and Wales,

To get together and concoct a scheme.

Scotland or the United Kingdom as a whole. It is not sufficient for a mere couple of enthusiasts to prepare the scheme; the authors must satisfy the Minister of Agriculture that they are " substantially representative " of persons who grow celery within the area, and the Minister must take into account the number of persons represented and the quantity of celery they produce.

Before he approves them, the Minister must publicise the proposals. He does this by a notice in the *London Gazette* and by such other means as he thinks may attract the notice of persons affected. In advertising the proposed Celery Marketing Scheme he must say where copies of the scheme may be inspected, or how they may be obtained. He must also give objectors not less than six weeks in which to submit their objections.

After that time has expired, he sits down to consider the scheme on its merits and in the light of objections or representations made by the anti-scheme celery producers. If any objections, other than frivolous ones, remain unresolved, the Minister must order a public inquiry to be held by a competent and impartial person. Indeed, he may set an inquiry afoot even if all the objections have been withdrawn. He himself may modify the scheme, provided he gives due notice.

The ultimate question the Minister must ask himself is: " Will the proposed scheme result in the more efficient production and marketing of celery? " If the answer is yes, he lays the draft scheme before both Houses of Parliament, with a report on the evidence that led him to believe that the persons sponsoring the scheme were " duly representative " of the celery industry. If both Houses approve, the Minister makes an order saying that the scheme will come into effect on a certain day.

As soon as the approval order is made, a suspensory period begins. This allows the interim board—whose members are named in the scheme—and others to make a register of all the celery producers in the area to be affected by the scheme. It entails the printing of explanatory notices and application forms in the press; at the same time the Ministry of Agriculture compile a list of all farmers believed to be celery growers and sends it to the board, and the board sends a registration form to each and all.

The next step is one on which marketing schemes have in real life fallen down: a poll on the question as to whether the Celery Marketing Scheme is to go ahead. To succeed, not less than two-thirds of the registered producers who bother to vote, both in numbers and in the total area of celery they grow, must say " aye ". Otherwise it ceases to take effect. Even though the poll is favourable, if at any time before the suspensory period is up it is proved that under half of the registered producers voted at the poll, the Minister must revoke the scheme.

The powers given to a marketing board include the right to buy the registered product, to sell, grade, pack or store it, to adapt it for sale, or to insure, advertise (Eata Sticka Celery) and transport it. It may require registered producers to sell all or part of their produce only to or through the agency of the board.

Once a scheme comes into operation, no producer may sell the registered product unless he has registered with the board or is exempted under the terms of the scheme. Exemption is very limited; in our fictitious case it might extend to growers who cultivate less than one-tenth of an acre of celery. A scheme cannot regulate the activities of distributors, nor can it control imports.

Defaulting producers may be called on to face a disciplinary committee, consisting of four to six board members with an independent barrister or solicitor as chairman. Those proved to have contravened the scheme may have penalties imposed upon them.

It is not always appreciated that a marketing board is a *producers'* organisation, which exists for their own interests and is boarded mainly by producer-retailers. It is not, in short, " another government racket " dominated by Them. That point established, we proceed to outline very briefly the particular features of the six marketing schemes in existence, in order of their appearance.

Hops Marketing Board—The Hops Marketing Scheme, which applies only to England, was approved in 1932 and the board, which has full trading powers, is the sole buyer of English hops. It regulates the supply by a quota system. Every year each producer is allotted a share of the quantity likely to be required by the brewers, the share being worked out according to a basic entitlement calculated on his farm's past performance.

The brewers' estimated demand, and the price they pay for the hops, are agreed by a committee of board and brewer representatives, under an independent chairman appointed by the Minister of Agriculture.

Milk Marketing Board—This was created in 1933 for England and Wales; a separate but similar scheme operates in Scotland. The board has full trading powers, and its main duty is the control of milk sales. All milk produced for sale by wholesale must be sold to the board, while producer-retailers require a board licence to sell milk. A producer may, however, sell milk to his farm workers or domestic servants, or milk from the home farm may be sold to estate workers, provided it is for their household consumption.

The M.M.B.'s big task is to arrange for the collection of milk from dairy farms and find a market for it. It translates into action the guaranteed price arrangements under the Agriculture Acts. While the government fixes the maximum retail prices and the distributive margin for milk sold for liquid consumption, the M.M.B. fixes the price of milk used for manufacturing purposes, after consulting buyers' representatives.

British Wool Marketing Board—This was born in 1950, and given full trading powers, including the sole right to buy fleece wool in the United Kingdom. It administers the government guarantee for wool arising under the Agriculture Acts, and performs its duty through agents employed to collect, grade and value fleece wool according to maximum prices announced in advance of the shearing season. It is then sold by auction, in competition with imported wool.

Tomato and Cucumber Marketing Board—This was instituted at about the same time as the last, and similarly applies to Great Britain as a whole. But by comparison with the full trading powers of the Wool Board it has limited "regulatory functions". For instance, it may determine the description and the terms on which registered producers may sell their tomatoes and cucumbers, or specify the merchants to whom alone they may be sold. It also runs a well thought-of service of market intelligence.

Potato Marketing Board—This again covers Great Britain, and was set up in 1955. It has powers to buy potatoes, but it is not the sole buyer. Among its considerable regulatory powers the board may prescribe the description, size, quality and terms of sale for potatoes sold by producers for human consumption. This is effected by estimating, as soon as possible after 1st September, the total quantity of potatoes likely to be available during the coming year, and comparing the figure with the quantity likely to be required for human consumption. The acreage farmers are tempted to grow is influenced by a system of differential levies.

The board also licenses merchants to whom alone potatoes may be sold. It has the right to prescribe minimum prices, and it implements the guarantee for potatoes as being one of the price review products under the Agriculture Acts.

British Egg Marketing Board—The youngest of the boards was born in 1956, and the egg marketing scheme applies to all the United Kingdom. It has full trading powers, and regulates the channel, price and description of all sales by registered producers— those with more than 50 head of poultry over 6 months of age. Licensed sales made to retailers direct are exempt, as are direct sales to consumers. In practice, registered producers sell their eggs to the board through packers, who pay them on the basis of minimum weekly prices fixed by the board and, as agents of the board, collect, grade and pack.

As well as regulating grades and packing, the board has powers to process eggs. It also implements the government guarantee for " Eggs (Hen and Duck in Shell) ".

Chapter 10

PESTS AND WEEDS

The law has for long fought a battle against certain fauna and flora which interfere too blatantly with the farmer's profit and peace of mind. In the war against pests the principal weapons today are the Agriculture Act, 1947, and the Pests Act, 1954.

To take them in order of appearance, section 98 of the former says that " if it appears to the Minister expedient that it is to do so for the purpose of preventing damage to crops, pasture, animal or human foodstuffs, livestock, trees, hedges, banks or other works on land, he may by notice in writing served on any person having the right to do so require that person to take, within such time as may be specified in the notice, such steps . . . as may be necessary for the killing, taking or destruction on land so specified of such animals or birds . . . as may be so specified or the eggs of such birds."

The service of this type of battle order is the responsibility of the local Ministry folk, but it is usually regarded as the last resort. As will have been seen, it is sent to a person entitled to kill the offending creatures, typically the tenant-farmer or owner-occupier, and takes the form of an order to get rid of the foxes or pigeons or sparrows currently ravaging his sheep or his spinneys within such and such a time.

The animals whose destruction can be so ordered are rabbits, hares or other rodents, deer, foxes and moles. The birds comprise wild birds which do not appear in the First Schedule to the Protection of Birds Act, 1954. (See page 200).

The Ministry cannot require any killing, taking or destruction which the law otherwise forbids; with the exception that game animals may be sentenced to death out of season. It is also provided that an order served by the Ministry will be a defence to any claim of proceedings against a tenant under the sporting rights clause in his tenancy agreement. The use of poisonous gas is permitted in burrows; and a game licence need not be especially obtained.

The farmer who ignores an order to destroy pests is liable on summary conviction to a fine of up to £25, and a further fine up to £5 a day for each day after conviction for as long as his inaction continues. Furthermore, the Ministry may authorise somebody

79

else to enter the land and do the job, the cost being recoverable from the defaulting party.

To assist in the destruction of animals, birds and their eggs condemned under this kind of order, the Ministry may provide various services and equipment, making such reasonable charges, if any, as they think fit.

Rabbit clearance

The rabbit is a sufficiently important pest to earn a section to itself. We have just seen that it is one of the creatures the Minister can command to be combated as one among other rodents. In making such provision for prevention of damage by pests, section 98 of the Agriculture Act, 1947, singles it out for further persecution: a farmer may be required to destroy not only the rabbits but their homes as well.

"Where it appears to the Minister . . . expedient for the purpose of preventing damage by rabbits to crops, pasture, trees, hedges, banks or any works on land, he may by notice in writing served on the occupier of land (or, in the case of unoccupied land, the person

Destroy not only the rabbits but their homes as well.

entitled to occupy it) require him to take on the land, within the time specified in the notice, such steps as may be so specified to destroy or reduce the breeding places or cover for rabbits or to exclude rabbits therefrom, or to prevent the rabbits living in any place on the land from spreading to or doing damage in any other place."

Every such notice must specify a time in which the occupier, or other interested person, may write back to object. The notice remains provisional during that time; that is to say, it is of no effect until confirmed by a further written notice.

Larger scale campaigns against the rabbit are authorised by the Pests Act, 1954. This gives the Minister power to designate blocks of land as " rabbit clearance areas ". Occupiers of land within the area are bound to take necessary steps to destroy wild rabbits which live on or resort to their land.

Before making the " rabbit clearance order " which sets a scheme in motion, the Ministry folk consult local interests: farmers, land-owners, foresters, farm workers and so on, and give due warning of their intentions by such agencies as the local press and village notice boards. Such notices will indicate the sort of " directions " the Ministry propose to include in the order, and allow at least 14 days during which interested persons can send in written objections or suggestions.

The occupiers of a rabbit clearance area may use any legitimate means of destruction, such as trapping, gassing or the use of long nets. But when it comes to shooting and the occupier does not have the full rights to shoot, he must get the consent of whoever owns the shooting rights before bringing on more guns than the Ground Game Acts allow him (see page 197). The owner of the rights may elect to shoot the rabbits himself instead of letting the occupier do so, but if he does not the occupier may ask the Ministry to authorise him to bring on additional guns to join the slaughter. The Ministry will only give their sanction if satisfied that the circumstances make necessary the use of more firearms than the Ground Game Acts allow an occupier to employ, that the occupier has tried to get permission from whoever has the right to kill and take the rabbits on his land, and that such permission has been unreasonably withheld.

Bringing land under a rabbit clearance order does not in any way prevent the Ministry from also serving on anyone having the right to kill vermin a notice requiring them to harass their rabbits under the 1947 Act provisions explained above. The war may be prosecuted through both lines of attack simultaneously.

Two paragraphs back we referred to " legitimate means " of destruction. However heartfelt the official desire to abolish the rabbit, the campaign has its Queensberry Rules. First, there is a ban on bacterial warfare, for it is an offence knowingly to use, or permit the use of, a rabbit infected with myxomatosis to spread the disease among uninfected ones. Secondly, there are restrictions on the use of spring traps.

Part II of the Pests Act, 1954, forbids the use of gin traps or of other spring traps not approved by the Minister of Agriculture. Equally, it is an offence to have a non-approved spring trap in one's possession for the purpose of killing or taking animals.

Approval is given to traps which have passed their tests by means of such orders as The Spring Traps Approval Order, 1957, which made legal for specified victims the Imbra, Fenn, Juby and Fuller traps. As inventors become more inventive and humane. other patterns may be added.

Spring traps for the killing or taking of rabbits may normally be set only in a rabbit hole, but the Minister may make exceptions by means of special regulations. Or again, through his local officers he may grant licences to use spring traps in a less limited manner than at bunny's front door. Such a licence may be included in a rabbit clearance order or in a notice served under the Agriculture Act, 1947.

The Small Ground Vermin Traps Order, 1958, allows rats, mice and other small vermin still to be legally destroyed by breakback traps, also by the kind of sprung trap commonly used for catching moles in their runs.

Rats and mice

The rabbit is not alone in being singled out for special outlawry; rats and mice, too, are the subject of special legislation. The combined effect of the Prevention of Damage by Pests Act, 1949, and the Prevention of Damage by Pests (Infestation of Food) Regulations, 1950, is to give a local authority power to order the occupier of land—agricultural or not—to take steps to destroy rats and mice or otherwise to keep the land free from such pests. Moreover, occupiers of land have a duty to notify the local authority of the presence of rats or mice in substantial numbers.

In practice the local authority serve a notice to take specific action against the pests and give the occupier a certain time in which to achieve results. Where the premises are let, a separate notice may be served on the owner, and if the land is agricultural the local authority must inform the C.A.E.C. of its actions.

If the person responsible ignores the notice, the local authority may themselves do what is required and recover the reasonable expense.

Another set of regulations applies where ricks are being threshed or dismantled. The Prevention of Damage by Pests (Threshing and Dismantling of Ricks) Regulations, 1950, apply to stacks of corn, beans, peas, tares or linseed. Before any such is dismantled it must be completely surrounded by a fence not less than 30 in. high, escape-proof against rats hemmed inside. If made of wire netting, the mesh must not exceed half an inch. While the rick is being worked on the owner must do all he can to destroy the rats and mice unhoused as a consequence.

The penalty for ignorance may be a fine of £20 for a first offence, or £50 for second and later offences.

INJURIOUS WEEDS

On the whole there is little the tidier neighbour can do about weeds coming on to his land, but the law has picked on five species, called " injurious weeds ", against which official action may be taken. They are spear thistle, creeping (or field) thistle, curled dock, broad-leaved dock and ragwort.

If the Minister of Agriculture (who acts through the C.A.E.C.) is satisfied that any of these injurious weeds are growing on any land, the Weeds Act, 1959, gives him power to serve the occupier with a notice requiring him, within a stated time, to take such action as may be necessary to prevent them from spreading. If the occupier is a tenant, a copy of the notice must be served on the landlord.

An occupier who unreasonably fails to comply may be fined up to £75 for a first offence, and up to £150 thereafter. And moreover, the C.A.E.C. may enter and do the work themselves, charging the occupier with the reasonable cost they are put to.

Chapter 11

DISEASES OF ANIMALS

No law can compel the farmer's animals to be healthy. There are many contagious diseases, however, whose spread can be checked by what often seem desperate remedies. Those measures are mainly bound up in the Diseases of Animals Act, 1950, which

No law can compel the farmer's animals to be healthy.

draws into its net ailing cattle, sheep, goats and all other ruminants, swine, chickens, ducks, guinea fowls, pigeons, pheasants, partridges, parrots, doves, peafowl and swans. Diseased bees are favoured by quite separate legislation.*

The Act applies to what are collectively called notifiable diseases, for the reason that if any visit his livestock the farmer must notify the police of the fact. A number of them are named in the Act, and the Minister of Agriculture may add to the list. On several occasions he has made additions for certain purposes. All in all they add up to a formidable catalogue; though in fact many of them have been unrecorded in Britain for years.

The more common diseases comprise anthrax; atrophic rhinitis in swine; foot-and-mouth disease in ruminants and swine; fowl pest in all kinds of poultry; swine fever; and certain forms of

---

* Foul Brood Disease of Bees Order, 1952 (No. 138).

tuberculosis in cattle, namely, tuberculosis of the udder, indurated udder or other chronic udder disease, tuberculosis emaciation, and chronic cough accompanied by definite clinical signs of TB. The success of the area eradication plan for tuberculosis, whereby the whole of England and Wales is an attested area, makes it unlikely that many cases of these forms of TB need to be anticipated.

More recent additions to the notifiable list include African horse sickness and psittacosis. The first is unknown in this country, but elsewhere it is fairly widespread. As a precaution the Importation of Horses, Asses and Mules (African Horse Sickness) (Prohibition) Order, 1960, put restrictions on bringing those animals into Britain from specified countries. Those imported from a country not on the list must be covered by a veterinary certificate stating that the disease has not existed in that country for at least twelve months.

Psittacosis, or ornithosis, was the subject of an order made in 1953 after an outbreak among ducks in Norfolk and Surrey. Its object was to prevent the introduction of the disease, and of fowl pest, by imported birds of the parrot family. The order extended the definition of "disease" under the Diseases of Animals Act, 1950, and provided for the detention and isolation of birds affected, or suspected of being affected, by psittacosis. Since the disease can be contracted by humans, it is rightly regarded as a danger to public health.

To complete the list, the following remain notifiable just, as it were, in case. As a consolation to the aspiring stock farmer, who by now may be teetering on the brink of adhering to arable husbandry,* we add in parentheses the dates of their last appearance.

Cattle plague, or rinderpest, in ruminating animals and swine (1877); epizootic lymphangitis in horses, asses and mules (1906); glanders and farcy in horses, asses and mules (1928); parasitic mange in horses, asses and mules (1948); pleuro-pneumonia in cattle (1898); rabies in ruminants, equine animals, swine, dogs and cats (1922); sheep pox (1850); and sheep scab (1952).

How the Act is enforced

County councils, and some of the larger borough councils, are required to appoint sub-committees to deal with notifiable diseases of animals, with a staff of inspectors sufficient to cope with the provisions of the 1950 Act and orders. Each county town houses

---

* Though even plants are subject to notifiable pests and diseases. The law requires that the Plant Health Branch of the Ministry of Agriculture must be notified of its existence; or suspected existence, of Colorado beetle; wart disease in potatoes; progressive verticillium wilt in hops; red core disease in strawberries; and fire blight disease in certain trees.

a staff of veterinary officers in the employment of the Ministry; they are available to take rapid action in emergency.

The official reaction to news of infection depends on the particular disease, the following being descriptive of the general routine.

Notification—A person who owns, or has under his charge, an animal actually or suspectedly suffering from a notifiable disease must notify the police with all reasonable haste. A vet who discovers the disease is under a similar obligation. The police then inform the Divisional Veterinary Officer of the Ministry, whose staff visit the farm or other premises to investigate.

Heavy penalties may fall upon a person who fails to report. Indeed, if charged with failure the court will presume that he knew of the existence of the disease until he is able to prove to them that he had no such knowledge, nor could he reasonably have discovered it.

Isolation—Diseased animals must be kept separate, as far as is practicable, from unaffected ones.

Infected areas—The Minister is empowered to make orders declaring that such and such a place is an infected area, harbouring such and such a disease. Within that area controls may be put on the movement of animals, carcasses, etc., and rules enforced as to the isolation and treatment of animals, the destruction or burial of carcasses. He may also require the cleansing and disinfection of fairs, markets, yards and sheds used for animals, and of vessels, vehicles and pens, and take other steps to check the spread of the disease.

Slaughter and compensation—The Minister's powers to order that notifiably diseased animals be put to death in some cases give him no alternative; in most there is a discretion. Thus he is bound to require the slaughter of all animals suffering from cattle plague and pleuro-pneumonia. He may—though not must— pronounce sentence of death upon animals which have been in contact with beasts so infected. Although foot-and-mouth and fowl pest are typically associated with the slaughter policy, the Act does not make it compulsory. In every case slaughter proceeds from the Minister using his discretionary rights to the full.

Where the Minister orders the slaughter of a diseased animal, its carcass becomes his property, and with it the right to say how it shall be disposed of. Alternatively he may suspend the death sentence until he has had time to take it away for observation or treatment.

The farmer whose beasts are slaughtered through the Diseases of

Animals Act is entitled to compensation. The rate varies according to the diseases and to whether the beast was affected or not. With unaffected animals the rate is typically their market value immediately before they were slaughtered; infected beasts may rank for half value.

Where a farmer has insured his livestock against loss from a notifiable disease, and insurance money becomes payable on a slaughtered animal, the company may deduct the amount of compensation received from the Ministry or local authority.

The Minister may withhold or reduce compensation where the owner has, in his opinion, offended against the Act or any order made under its powers. If, for instance, he tried to conceal a notifiable disease his prospects of receiving compensation after discovery and slaughter of the affected animals would be slight.

Sheep dipping

Sheep scab has been cited above as a notifiable disease. It is caused by a mite which spreads rapidly and itchily, and is transmitted through being rubbed off against posts and fences by irritated sheep, from which it is transferable to others. Because of the wastage it causes, the Minister of Agriculture has powers to order the compulsory dipping of sheep or the use of some other remedy.

To make sure that such orders are carried out, Ministry inspectors, or people from the County Council or other authority, may go on any farm to inspect the sheep and if necessary instruct the farmer to take action.

The local authority may make provision for dipping places or portable tanks, and charge the farmers for using them.

Chapter 12

MILK AND DAIRIES

But the dairy farmer and the vineyard proprietor will maintain that their products are good for you. So they are; but only one of them benefits from keeping. Milk is potentially a treacherous thing, much affected by dirt and a heavenly home for bacteria. To ensure that it is produced with a minimum of danger to the consumer, the dairy farmer who wishes to remain in business must subscribe

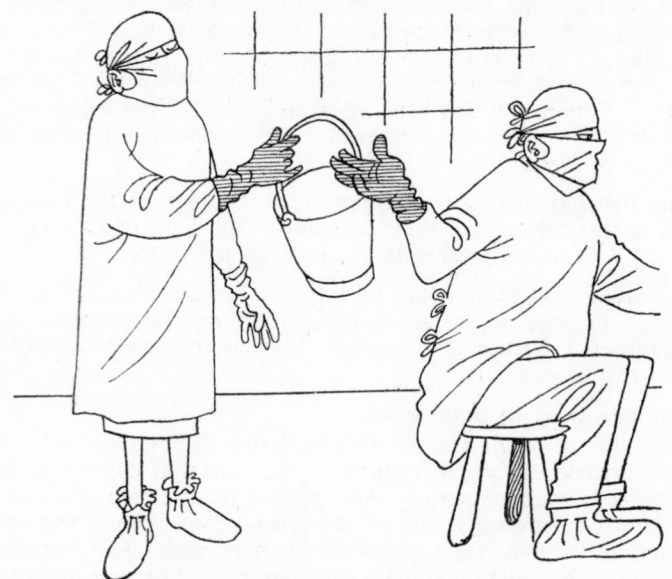

Must subscribe to a code of cleanliness.

to a code of cleanliness. The requirements that make up that code are consolidated in The Milk and Dairies (General) Regulations, 1959, into which we will now quarry.

Registration

Before any farmer can trade as a dairy farmer, or use any premises as a dairy farm, he must get himself and his premises registered. To do this he applies to his Divisional Office of the Ministry of Agriculture. One of the first things they will want to

89

know is whether the premises measure up to the standards required by the regulations—standards of building design, cleanliness and so on—which are discussed later in this chapter. If they do not, registration will be refused and the Ministry stand their ground until the shortcomings are made good.

If there is a change of occupier on premises already registered, or if a registered producer transfers his herd to an unregistered farm, registration is normally granted to the new occupier. But the Ministry will require him to correct any contraventions of the regulations within a stated period; otherwise his registration may be cancelled.

If the Ministry folk feel that the regulations cannot be complied with, they may refuse registration. In that case they must formally notify the applicant of their intention to refuse; and the applicant has a right to state his objection before a tribunal consisting of a chairman and two other members, appointed by the Minister of Agriculture. The chairman is an independent person; of the other two, one is appointed from a panel nominated by the National Farmers' Union and the Milk Marketing Board, the other—who represents the consumers' interests—after consultation with the Ministry of Health.

The tribunal in due time report their findings of the facts to the Ministry, who make their decision in the light of that report coupled with any representations made by the farmer.

A similar right to be heard by a tribunal comes about when the Ministry propose to cancel a registration on the grounds that the registered farmer is no longer playing the game according to the regulations.

Requirements as to buildings

The body of regulations relating to design of buildings is by no means so stringent as to frighten off the potential dairyman; for each there is a simple reason. As a general requirement, the buildings in which cows are milked must not be so situated or constructed as to give rise to contamination of milk. For instance, such sources of contamination as drainage effluent or manure heaps must be kept at considerably more than udder's-length away.

Next, the air in the milking house must be kept fresh. This, of course, is a matter of proper ventilation. And windows and artificial light must be adequate to let the milker see clearly what he is doing.

Any part of the floor liable to be soiled by cows must be impervious to water and so constructed that it can be easily washed down. It should be sloped and provided with channels, so that liquid waste can be conveyed to a suitable drain outside the building, and so to a suitable place of disposal.

As to the walls, such parts as are liable to be soiled or infected, e.g., by the indelicate act of cows which cannot wait until they get outside, must be rendered impervious so that they can readily be washed.

Every registered dairy farm must have its milk room or farm dairy, where milk may be properly strained, cooled and stored and the equipment sterilised. Except where alternative arrangements are approved, the milk must be taken there as soon as possible after milking. As with the dairy, the milk room should be properly lighted and ventilated, the floor made impervious and laid to a slight slope leading to a trapped drain. If oil or solid fuel are used for water heating and steam raising a separate boiler house is required, one having no direct communication with the milk room.

All these washing requirements suggest that you cannot produce clean milk without plenty of water, and indeed the regulations insist that there must be a suitable and sufficient supply, and that precautions must be taken against its becoming polluted.

Cleanliness in the buildings is hammered home. They must always be cleanly maintained, the access and surroundings kept free of accumulated dung or other offensive matter. Pigs or poultry may not be kept in a milking house, nor in any room with direct access to it. No animals may be kept in any room where milk is handled or where the milking equipment is stored, nor in any room which has direct communication with it.

Requirements as to production

The milk regulations do not confine their rules to the layout and cleansing of buildings. They have much else to say about methods of milking, and they lay on the farmer a duty to make their requirements familiar to all his employees engaged in or around the dairy.

Flying dust is a notorious menace to milk; consequently no dry bedding, hay or other dusty matter must be moved in the milking house half an hour before milking begins nor, naturally, during milking. The milker must garb himself in a clean and washable overall and head covering; any cuts or abrasions he bears must be bandaged or otherwise covered. Before milking he must thoroughly wash and dry his hands, and see that throughout the milking session they are kept clean. As to the herd, before ever a drop is extracted, each cow's flanks, tail, udder and teats must be cleaned, and the udder and teats must be kept clean so long as milking lasts. While in action the milker must refrain from smoking or spitting; no such prohibition extends to the cow.

The foremilk of each cow must be separately drawn into a receptacle, so that it can be looked at for such telltale signs as mastitis clots. It must then be disposed of in such a way that it cannot be blamed for passing on infection. Then, while the new-drawn milk is awaiting removal to the milk room, the vessel that holds it must be covered.

In the dairy the most pressing need is for cooling, which must be done with no more loss of time than it takes first to strain the milk. The purpose of cooling is to check the growth of bacteria, which prefer warmth for multiplying in. To satisfy the regulations the milk must be brought down to 50°F. or to within 5°F. of the temperature of the cooling water.

As to utensils, just any old pail will not do. No receptacle or appliance may be used unless it is capable of being readily cleansed. And before any vessel is used for containing milk, or any appliance brought into contact with milk, it must immediately be brought into a state of thorough cleanliness. The regulations prescribe the drill to be followed in cleansing dairy equipment: they are all well established. First, thorough rinsing with cold or tepid water; next, washing with hot water, with or without added detergents; finally, sterilisation with steam, boiling water, or one of the chemicals officially approved by the Ministry of Agriculture and the Ministry of Health.*

Requirements as to distribution

These concern the despatch and conveyance of milk. Every vessel in which it is despatched by road or rail must be marked or labelled with the name and address of the person from whom it was sent; and every container must have a lid without openings, and so fitted that no dirt, dust or rainwater can get in. Where the milk is put up in bottles or cartons, they may be filled and closed only on registered premises.

All practicable precautions must be taken to prevent milk from being needlessly exposed to heat and from being contaminated. For example, a roadside stand where milk is dumped to await collection should reasonably offer some natural or artificial shade. As to bottles and cartons of milk, they must not be left beside the road while awaiting onward delivery.

Lastly, vehicles used for the carriage of milk must be kept clean. It is forbidden to transport live animals and birds as fellow passengers to the milk load. And if a vehicle has been carrying offensive matter, it must be cleansed and disinfected before it carries its next cargo of milk.

---

* These are listed in the Ministry of Agriculture Advisory Leaflet No. 422
—*Cleansing and Chemical Sterilisation of Farm Dairy Utensils.*

Infection spread through milk

Since sick humans may pass on their afflictions through milk, the regulations include certain precautions aimed at lessening such risks. They amount to this:

If a person engaged on dairy work becomes aware that he or a member of his household is suffering from a notifiable disease,* the dairy farmer must notify the medical officer of health for the district in which the premises are situated. The medical officer has the power to examine such persons and to stop their doing dairy work as long as the risk of infection lasts.

If a medical officer of health knows or suspects that a supply of milk is infected, he may either hold up the sale or use of that milk, or require it to be treated in such a way as to make it safe.

DESIGNATED MILK

Milk which is sold as it comes from the cow, with no other treatment than straining and cooling, is known as raw milk. The dairy farmer or dealer with higher aspirations may apply for a licence to sell " designated " milk. In this event he, in effect, guarantees that his milk reaches a specified standard of purity, his reward being a higher price.

The Milk (Special Designations) Regulations, 1960, which consolidate the rules relating to production, testing and sale, acknowledge three classes of designated milk: tuberculin tested, pasteurised and sterilised.

Licences to producers of T.T. milk are granted by the Divisional Offices of the Ministry of Agriculture; but dealers' licences to sell designated milk are, with some exceptions, the responsibility of the local authorities who deal with the far-reaching Food and Drugs legislation.

A producer or retailer who wishes to obtain a licence must first of all be complying with the relevant sections of the Milk and Dairies Regulations. In addition, the milk to be sold under a special designation must satisfy tests which are laid down in detail in the Special Designation Regulations of 1960.

Under the Food and Drugs Act, 1955, orders can be made to apply to specified areas whereby only specially designated milks may be retailed, other than as catering sales, or by a dairy farmer

---

* To prevent their pestering the M.O.H. each time they have a headache, we would inform the over-zealous that notifiable diseases in humans comprise smallpox, diphtheria, membranous croup, erysipelas, scarlet fever, and the fevers known as typhus, typhoid, enteric or relapsing. For notifiable diseases in animals see Chapter 11.

to persons employed on the farm, or with the special consent of the Ministry of Agriculture if it is impracticable for specially designated milk to be supplied. The areas in which these requirements apply are known as specified areas. At the present time almost the whole of England and Wales has become specified, and it is only a matter of time before the whole country is affected by these orders and only designated milk will be sold.

PART III

MASTER AND MAN

Labour disputes, strikes and lockouts, differentials and demarcation problems—all the familiar tribulations of industry seem to belong to another world.   No doubt the close and friendly relationships between farmers and their workpeople make this part of the book almost unnecessary.   But here, as elsewhere, farmers have their special problems.

All the familiar tribulations of industry.

In this part we begin with an outline of the law of Master and Servant.   Then we shall see how Parliament has in recent years intervened to make provision for a basic minimum wage, for insurance and for the safety and welfare of workers employed in **agriculture.**

Chapter 13

MASTER AND SERVANT

Between a farmer and his employees, the basis of the relationship is a contract, no matter how informal, recognised by the law, whereby the servant agrees to serve in return for the master's promise to pay wages or make some other form of reward. The relationship of master and servant is quite distinct from every other kind of legal relationship, such as partnership or agency, although there may be points of similarity; and certain fixed rules of common law attach to it. For example, the law will presume, in the absence of clear provision to the contrary, that the master has agreed to pay wages. If nothing is said about wages at the beginning of the employment—and it is surprising how frequently this happens in practice—the court will presume that the worker agreed to serve for a reasonable wage, or " *quantum meruit* ", that is to say, as much as he deserved. In these circumstances the court will be entitled to consider evidence about prevailing conditions and wages for the particular work and fix an appropriate sum. There is one other important respect in which a contract of service differs from other contracts, namely, that " specific performance " is not available as a remedy. At common law, contracts in general can be enforced either: —

(a) by an award of damages for " breach of contract " if a term of the contract has been broken; or

(b) by an order for specific performance, to remedy a breach or to prevent an anticipated breach.

An order for specific performance simply means that the court will require the offending party to carry out his part of the bargain on the terms to which he agreed; if he fails to do so he may in the last resort be imprisoned. In the case of a contract of service, however, the court will award damages but refuse specific performance, in view of the personal nature of the contract.

In practical terms this means that where, for example, a farmer takes on a casual worker to hoe and single a specified field of sugar beet, then if the worker downs tools when the job is half done and refuses to carry on, the farmer will be entitled only to damages by way of redress. The damages, i.e., the loss arising directly from the breach of the agreement, would be small in practice— probably limited to the cost of advertising for another man.

The relationship of master and servant begins when the contract of service becomes operative: in other words when an offer on either side has been made and accepted and the servant has actually entered into the master's employment. Except in one case the contract may be ended only by notice. If no express provision is made a reasonable notice is required, and this has been interpreted by the courts to mean a period equal to the period between successive instalments of wages. Farm workers are almost invariably paid weekly; accordingly in their case a full week's notice is required, terminating on the day when wages are normally payable. The one case in which notice will not be required is when the servant has done something to justify instant dismissal, such as wilful disobedience.

Implied duties of the servant

Apart from the express terms of the contract there are certain implied conditions at common law. The servant must give personal service, i.e., he must not delegate his duties to somebody else. He must obey lawful and reasonable orders; he must serve honestly and faithfully, carefully and competently; and he must account for any incidental profits. An interesting example of this last rule is provided by the case of *Reading v. Attorney-General*, 1950. In that case Reading was a British Army sergeant who contrived to "earn" several thousands of pounds by using his position to secure immunity from search for trucks containing contraband. It was held by the House of Lords that Reading was a trustee for the Government of the money which had come into his hands in this way, and that he must accordingly account for it as an incidental profit of his employment in the service of His Majesty. On the same principle the servant will be a trustee for the master of any inventions or discoveries made during the master's time and with his materials. (See *British Celanese v. Moncrieff*, 1943). Applied to farming, this would mean that if, for example, a farm worker, being of an inventive turn of mind, designed a revolutionary kind of feed-hopper out of his master's milk churns during working hours, the patent rights would vest in the farmer.

Implied duties of the master

In addition to his obligation to pay wages, the master is under a duty to indemnify the servant against any losses or expenses incurred by him in carrying out the service, provided that there is no neglect, default or illegality on the servant's part. The master is also under a general duty to take reasonable care for the servant's safety. This duty was discussed in the House of Lords in *Wilsons and Clyde Coal Company v. English*, 1937, where the master's duty was said to be threefold: —

(a) he must provide a competent staff;

(b) he must provide suitable materials and plant and machinery must be adequately maintained; and

(c) he must ensure that buildings or premises used are reasonably safe as work places.

In short, this means that an employer's duty to his workers is to take care in all these three respects. Only by doing so can he satisfy his general obligation at common law to provide a " safe system of work ".

More recently, as we shall see in Chapter 15, statute has added substantially and in detail to the employers' duties in relation to a safe system of work. In some cases the Farm Safety Regulations place workers under an obligation to warn their employers of certain dangers. At common law if the worker is injured as a result of some danger known to him but unknown to the employer, he may well be held to have been contributorily negligent if he fails to give the warning, which would have the effect of reducing his damages. If, however, the master knows of the danger and allows it to continue, he cannot plead that because the servant also knew of it he had consented to taking the risk. This is the effect of the decision in *Smith v. Baker*, 1891. In that case a workman in a cutting was injured by a stone falling from a crane which periodically swung over his head. It was argued for the employers that because the workman knew of the risk and continued working, he had in effect assented to the risk in much the same way as a sportsman playing in a dangerous game. The court, however, held that mere knowledge of the risk was something very different from assenting to it, and held the employers liable. The decision might perhaps have been different if the workman had been in a position to prevent the danger.

Master's liability for the servant's wrongful acts

As we have seen, a servant is clothed with a general authority to act on his master's behalf. In view of this the courts have developed a doctrine known as the doctrine of "vicarious liability", by virtue of which the master will be liable for the torts, or civil wrongs, of the servant committed " within the course of his employment ". The master for this purpose stands in the shoes of the servant, and he may avail himself of any defence which would have been available to the servant. There is a wealth of case law on the meaning of the words " in the course of the employment ". It has been held that the wrongful act may be within the employment even if it has been expressly forbidden by the master, but it is well established that the master will not be liable if the servant was not really doing his job at all but had " gone off on a frolic of his own ". For the master to succeed in escaping liability on this ground means that the servant must have gone on a private jaunt quite separate from his master's business; it would not be sufficient if he had merely made a detour on an authorised journey.

Examples from the decided cases may help to illustrate some of these points. In *Lloyd v. Grace Smith and Co.*, 1912, a solicitor's managing clerk fraudently induced a client to convey property to him, then absconded with the proceeds. It was held that the employers would be liable even though the tort was committed for the servant's own benefit. In *Limpus v. London General Omnibus Company*, 1862, a bus driver, contrary to express orders, drove so as to obstruct a rival bus which overturned as a result. His employers were held liable. By contrast, in *Beard v. London General Omnibus Company*, 1900, in the absence of the driver the conductor of the bus drove it, and by his negligence injured the plaintiff. The employer was held not liable, for driving a bus is not within the scope of a conductor's employment. In *Poland v. Parr*, 1927, the driver of a cart struck a boy under the mistaken impression that the boy was stealing sugar from the cart. The boy fell under a wheel which crushed his foot. It was held that the employer was liable, as the servant had implied authority to protect his master's property in an emergency and thus was acting within the scope of his employment. The fact that the servant would also have been liable criminally for an assault was held to be irrelevant. As a final example, in *Bayley v. Manchester, Sheffield and Lincolnshire Railway*, 1873, an officious porter injured the plaintiff by violently pulling him out of a carriage in the mistaken belief that he was in the wrong train. It was held that the Railway Company was liable, since the porter was merely doing in an over-enthusiastic fashion something of the class of things which he was employed to do.

When servant turns competitor

On entering into a contract of service it frequently happens that the master would wish to prevent the servant from using, at some future date, and in competition with the master's business, any special knowledge or information which he may gain from that employment. When making conditions of this sort in service agreements, the parties must guard against making them too sweeping, otherwise they will be unenforceable. If, for example, a producer-retailer of milk in engaging a roundsman asked him to sign a written service agreement under which the roundsman undertook " not to take any employment in the milk trade anywhere in the British Isles for a period of 20 years after the termination of the agreement ", the clause would be struck out as void on grounds of public policy. Drafted thus widely its effect is clearly to deprive the roundsman of his livelihood in that particular trade. Such a clause would be enforceable, however, if it were made subject to reasonable limits as to time and place, e.g., " for five years in the Isle of Ely ". Such clauses, if they are reasonable and therefore enforceable, form part of the goodwill of the business and they may be enforced by a purchaser of the goodwill.

Chapter 14

AGRICULTURAL WAGES AND SERVICE COTTAGES

Most of the law touching farm workers' wages is contained in the Agricultural Wages Act, 1948, but before turning to it we might briefly mention two provisions of the Truck Acts, 1831–96. Their main purpose was to preclude all forms of payment in kind.

The first is that all wages of manual workers including those working on the land must be paid in current coin of the realm; the other that any condition imposed as to the person with whom or the place or manner in which the wages are to be spent is void.

Forms of payment in kind.

The first requirement has to be read subject to the Payment of Wages Act, 1960, which makes it lawful for wages to be paid by cheque at the written request of the employee.

THE AGRICULTURAL WAGES ACT, 1948

This Act provides for the periodic review of wages paid throughout the agricultural industry. The Minister of Agriculture may make regulations prescribing a statutory minimum wage, and it is an offence to pay less than the minimum wage, minus the prescribed value of any benefits or advantages given by the employer.

It operates through the Agricultural Wages Board as the central authority for England and Wales. The Board consists of 21 members. Eight of them represent employers; another eight represent employees; the remaining five, of whom one must be a woman, are appointed by the Minister as independent members.

In practice the Minister's members include a legally qualified Chairman, and the deliberations of the Board usually take the form of a semi-legal proceeding. In the current inflationary state of the economy, it is unlikely that the Board would be required to consider other than an increase in wages; consequently it is the farm workers who present the case.

When the farm workers' unions propose to apply for a wage increase they notify the Wages Board at one of their routine monthly meetings. Next month the Board will have been furnished with written details of the workers' case. Facts and figures to illustrate their claim may be supported verbally by the workers' representatives on the Board, so that the whole thing is thrashed out there and then. By the following meeting the employers' representatives will have set down their counter-arguments, and this is their opportunity to answer objections in person.

Another month passes, and this time the Board get down to their decision, during which process the independent members play the part of conciliators. After matters are put to the vote, details of new rates and conditions must be published in the form of Proposals. The Act requires that at least 14 days must elapse from the date of publication, to allow objections to be lodged with the Secretary to the Board.

Such objections as are received usually cover ground which the Board have well trodden, and in practice this 14-day respite is little more than a formality. Finally, the Proposals are confirmed and reprinted as Orders applying, with minor specific exceptions, to the whole of the country, from an appointed date.

The Board are obliged to fix minimum rates for time-work; in addition they may, and customarily do, fix minimum rates for piece-work and paid holidays. In the latter respect farm workers generally are entitled to two weeks' holiday with pay or, where they have completed less than 12 months' service, one day's paid holiday for each complete month in the employment. The Wages Board's orders also prescribe for the reckoning of various benefits and advantages in lieu of cash, thus creating an important exception to the general requirement of the Truck Acts about " current coin of the realm ". Bed and board, accommodation in cottages, free milk, eggs, or potatoes are all examples of the benefits which may be allowed, but the " prices " may vary from county to county.

Much of the day to day work in connection with farm workers' wages and benefits is performed by Agricultural Wages Committees which exist in each county or for certain combinations of counties. They exercise their functions in accordance with directions given by the Board.

Wages during sickness

A service agreement frequently provides that no wages shall be payable during the worker's absence through sickness. The Court of Appeal, in *Smart v. Spencer,* 1948, held that such a clause was valid, and that an employer was therefore under no obligation to make any payment in respect of weeks' wages where an employee was absent intermittently over a period of several months. Where, however, the illness begins in the course of a working week, the employer is probably obliged to pay the full statutory wage for the initial broken week. What happens afterwards must depend on the agreement.

THE TIED COTTAGE

Without wishing to get involved in the political issues, it seems clear that the system of tied cottages—or, as they should strictly be called, " service occupations "—is likely to persist. There are obvious advantages both for farmers and farm workers in a system which enables them to offer or be offered virtually free accommodation which goes with the job. The legal difficulties here, however, are not to be underestimated, and many a farmer has woken up too late to discover that his worker or the worker's next of kin have entrenched themselves, perhaps unwittingly, as tenants under the protection of the Rent Acts.

At common law the notion of service occupation is by no means confined to agriculture. The manager of a public house belonging to a brewer is a service occupier, the nursing staff in hospitals are service occupiers of their rooms; many other examples could be found. The common link between all these is that the employee occupies the premises *for the better performance of his duties under the service agreement,* and it is always advisable that this should be clearly written into the service agreement itself.

It is sometimes galling to a farmer who has an attractive cottage available, which he could no doubt let in the open market at a substantial rent, to find that its value to him is limited in effect to a paltry 6s. a week. On occasion the worker himself is agreeable to paying more than the statutory figure. The question then arises, whether by making two quite separate agreements—

(a) a service agreement in which the farmer agrees to pay at least the statutory minimum wage; and

(b) a tenancy agreement in which the worker agrees to take a tenancy of the cottage and pay an economic rent for it—

the parties can, so to speak, contract out of the artificial limit upon the value of the cottage imposed by the Agricultural Wages Act and orders.

Precisely this situation arose in *Williams v. Smith,* 1934. The case turned on the interpretation of the Agricultural Wages (Regulation) Act, 1924, as to board and lodging, which was one of the permitted "benefits and advantages" under that Act. The facts were that an agricultural worker was paid his full statutory wages, as required. Under a separate agreement with his employer, he paid him back £1 each week for boarding and lodging with him, 15s. being the maximum permitted figure under the then legislation as the value of board and lodging which could be reckoned as payment of wages instead of payment in cash. It was admitted that the worker was free to lodge elsewhere; indeed the employer would have preferred him to do so. The court, however, held that the farmer could not escape the consequences of the Act simply by going through the procedure of making two separate agreements, if the granting of the benefit or advantage was really part and parcel of the contract of service. Here there was, in substance, one transaction to which the Act must be strictly applied.

This case should be contrasted with *Long Eaton Co-operative Society v. Smith,* 1949, in which the facts were quite different. In that case an agricultural worker was employed by the society and paid the statutory wage. For the first two years of his employment he found his own accommodation; then he accepted a tenancy of a house belonging to the society, on the understanding that they would be entitled to possession at four weeks' notice, " should I cease under any cause to be employed by the society as a farm labourer ". The worker remained in the house for some four years until the termination of his employment, paying rents of between 8s. 10d. and 9s. 6d. per week. Those were the rents permitted under the Rent Restrictions Acts, but they were considerably in excess of what would have been permitted by way of deduction from the man's wages.

In an action in the County Court for possession of the cottage, the worker counterclaimed for the rent he alleged he had overpaid in excess of the amount permitted under the Agricultural Wages Act. The case went to the Court of Appeal, which distinguished it from the earlier decision in *Williams v. Smith* and held that in the present case there were two quite separate agreements. " The court ", it was said, " must look at the whole terms of the employment and then, taking them as a whole, see whether or not the minimum is paid. They may be found in one document or two, in one contract or in two contracts. Whenever found the whole must be looked at to see whether or not the minimum requirements of the Act are complied with. It is altogether different in the present case. The letting of this house was not one of the terms of the employment, it was not part and parcel of the transaction when the worker was employed, as in *Williams v. Smith;* it was a completely separate and independent transaction and such a transaction is not touched by the Act at all. The defendant was receiving his full minimum wage throughout the period. Two years after he entered the employment the employer let him this house. He paid less rent than he had been paying for his previous house and he only paid the rent allowed by the Rent Restrictions Acts. In those circumstances it seems to me to be wrong to say that there is any offence against the Act."

THE RENT ACTS

It follows from what we have said that if the worker is merely allowed to occupy the cottage as part and parcel of his rights under the service agreement, he will be a mere service occupier and, of course, the deduction from the wage in respect of the cottage will be limited to the statutory amount. If, however, the worker is permitted for any reason (as in the *Long Eaton* case) to take a tenancy of the cottage, then the Rent Restrictions Acts will apply to such a tenancy. The effect of this in the case of a tenancy granted before 1957 would be twofold:

(a) the rent would be subject to control; and

(b) the tenant would be protected by restrictions upon the owner's right to serve notice to quit.

The effect of the restrictions under both paragraphs (a) and (b) was severely limited by the Rent Act, 1957. However, they are still in force in cases to which the Rent Restrictions Acts still apply, and the degree of security of tenure conferred upon tenants in such cases is such that in practice the landlord finds it impossible to get possession, unless he can show that he would suffer greater hardship by the refusal of possession than the tenant would suffer by having to quit.

The Rent Act, 1957, entirely freed from the effects of the Rent Restrictions Acts two broad classes of lettings:

(a) lettings under new agreements entered into after July, 1957; and

(b) all lettings of dwelling-houses having a rateable value of more than £30 (outside London).

Thus, where a house or cottage of small rateable value was let to an agricultural worker for a weekly tenancy before July, 1957, the Rent Restrictions Acts would apply to such a tenancy.

In conclusion, there is one general provision of the Act of 1957 applying to all lettings of dwelling-houses which deserves to be mentioned. This is section 16, which provides that where a dwelling-house is let on a weekly tenancy, the tenancy may not in any circumstances be terminated by less than four weeks' notice.

Chapter 15

NATIONAL INSURANCE

Our national insurance scheme, in its present form, began in 1948, and has been growing a little more involved ever since. This chapter is principally concerned with one aspect: the farmer's responsibilities as an employer.

Participation in national insurance is compulsory for all persons over school leaving age (subject to certain concessions). School leaving age is the end of the school term following the 15th birthday, or the 15th birthday if it happens during a school holiday. The purpose of national insurance is to compensate them during illness, injury, unemployment and retirement. It provides three things:

(1) Flat-rate weekly cash benefits during sickness, unemployment, widowhood and retirement from regular work. This is the main Flat-rate National Insurance Scheme.

(2) Cash benefits, under the Industrial Injuries Scheme, for those who, because of an accident at work or one of the prescribed industrial diseases, are disabled or unable to work.

(3) Additional retirement pensions under the Graduated Pensions Scheme.

These schemes are in fact separate, and it is not every person who contributes to all three. For contribution purposes, however, national insurance, industrial insurance and national health service contributions are covered by one stamp.

Insured persons are split into three groups: employed, self-employed, non-employed. The schemes they come into, the contributions they make and the benefits they obtain vary according to the group.

Class 1, the employed people, number the majority of folk who do any work.

Class 2, the self-employed, include those in business on their own account—farmers, among others—and those who work for money but not under the control of an employer.

Class 3 embraces the non-employed persons, all those who do not belong to Class 1 or Class 2. It includes the retired, the between-jobbers, the too rich to bother and the congenital layabout.

All three classes pay flat-rate contributions, which include a national health service contribution. Those in Class 1 also make an industrial injuries contribution and (unless they are contracted out) if they are over 18 and earn more than £9 a week, graduated pension contributions.

Whereas national insurance is partially paid for by taxes and by interest on the investment of insurance funds, most of the millions it runs into comes from the contributions of insured people and employers. In the case of employees, it is the employer's responsibility to see that their contributions are made and to add his share to them. For flat-rate and industrial insurance he deducts from the weekly pay-packet the worker's share, buys the appropriate stamps from the post office and sticks them on the employee's card. Graduated pension contributions are similarly deducted, but paid in a monthly sum to the Collector of Taxes. This and other differences make it expedient to deal from now on with the "normal" national insurance and the graduated pension scheme separately.

FLAT-RATE NATIONAL INSURANCE

In general, a farmer must pay a flat-rate contribution for any farm worker over school-leaving age who works for him under his control. Each employee is given a contribution card, which lasts a year and has a stamp-shaped space for every week. The "contribution week" begins and ends at midnight on Sunday, and an employer is generally required to pay a contribution for each such week of his worker's employment. The contribution rates for master and man (or woman) vary according to age and sex.

Employed married women and widows

The main national insurance flat-rate contributions cover a man's wife and family as well as himself, therefore married women in employment need not pay for this part of the scheme unless they so wish. They are obliged, however, to make industrial injuries contributions and contribute to the graduated pension scheme. Employed widows in general contribute on all three counts, but certain classes can choose not to pay flat-rate insurance. They are: those entitled either to widow's pension at the rate of 57s. 6d. a week or more under the War Pensions or Industrial Injuries Schemes, or to widow's benefits under the National Insurance Scheme—that is to say, widow's allowance, widowed mother's allowance or widow's pension other than the widow's ten-shilling pension.

A woman who does not contribute to the full flat-rate insurance scheme is given a certificate of exemption, which takes the form of either a label (C.F.16) attached to her contribution card or a card marked "special". This authorises her employer to pay contributions at special rates, but in no way exempts him from paying his share as employer.

Men and women of riper years

The minimum age for receiving retirement pensions is 65 for men and 60 for women. But until a man reaches 70 or a woman 65, the pension is dependent on retirement from regular work. Men between 65 and 70 and women aged 60 to 65 continue to pay national insurance in the usual way unless they have retired.

Retirement as such means giving up all forms of paid work. An employee may qualify for the modified description "treated as retired", no matter how many hours of work he puts in, if his weekly net earnings are expected to be less than 71s. a week. A person who intends to exceed these earnings may still be treated as retired provided the work he does is not inconsistent with retirement, a question that may have to be decided in consultation with the local Ministry of Pensions and National Insurance officials.

Employees treated as retired but working for an employer pay only their part of the industrial injuries contributions. The employer must pay his share of the full flat-rate contributions. Neither party is called on to pay graduated pension contributions.

Where after retirement a worker returns to full-time employment, he is still regarded as retired for national insurance purposes unless he cancels his retirement and exchanges his special card for an ordinary one.

Occasional, casual workers, etc.

We have seen that most farm workers come into Class 1; for them the employer pays flat-rate insurance without complications. We now consider some non-regular workers he may employ. They are not in Class 1, and their employer is liable only for industrial injuries contributions on their behalf. The ordinary national insurance contribution they must see to themselves, at the self-employed or non-employed rate.

(a) Very short periods of employment

An employer is responsible for paying his share of the industrial injuries contribution for anyone employed by him: —

(i) for not more than 8 hours in a contribution* week, where the worker does not *normally* render him service for more than 8 hours a week. If, on the other hand, an employee who normally works 8 hours or less per week for him does more than 8 hours' work in a particular week, then a Class 1 contribution is due for that week.

Thus, old Bill who comes in for an hour every morning to prime the pumps normally puts the boss to the expense of the employer's share of industrial injuries contribution only. However, for that cold week when he had trouble in starting them and laboured for 16 hours by the church clock, the boss would have to stamp his card as he does for the regular staff.

(ii) where the employee works not more than 4 hours in a contribution week and the employment is a continuing one in which more than 8 hours' work is normally done each week. As an example, if part-time Jack normally works 12 hours a week doing relief milking for Farmer Herd, but takes the rest of one particular week off after two hours in the dairy on Monday, then Farmer Herd's national insurance duty towards Jack that week is limited to his share of the industrial injuries contribution.

(b) Sunday workers

Last Gathering-Sunday Wandering Joe helped with the harvest and, liking the place, worked his way well into the following week. Sunday is the last day of the national insurance contribution week, and where a worker serves his employer only on that last day of the week, and continues into the next contribution week, his employer need, for that Sunday-only week contribute no more than his industrial injuries share.

(c) Workers ending on Monday

If Wandering Joe had begun his harvest help on a Friday or Saturday and continued into, but not beyond, a normal day's work on the following Monday, his employer would have to see that Joe's card was stamped (a) for the full flat-rate insurance for the week ending at midnight on the intervening Sunday, but (b) for industrial injuries only for the Monday-only week. Rule (b) does not apply where employment starts earlier than Friday.

(d) Farm pupils and their ilk

An apprentice who receives no remuneration in cash or kind (e.g., board and lodging) needs to be compulsorily covered only for industrial injuries, and his employer is liable for the whole cost, the apprentice's share and his own. If he is over 18 the unpaid, unrewarded apprentice retains his contribution card so that he may, if he wishes, participate in the flat-rate scheme, wholly at his own expense and at the non-employed rate. In such event the employer pays the industrial injuries contributions on a separate card distinguished by a special label. When the employer's liability for separate payment of industrial injuries contributions ceases, he gives the card he holds to the apprentice, who must return it to his local Pensions and National Insurance office—unless he goes to another employer on the same unrewarded terms, who takes on the industrial injuries responsibilities.

(e) Harvest help, and that sort of thing

People employed as occasionals in corn harvesting, potato planting or lifting, or the picking of hops, peas, beans or fruit are excluded from Class 1. The farmer employing them is liable only for industrial injuries contributions. If such a worker is ordinarily engaged in agriculture, horticulture or forestry, however, or if he produces evidence that he is ordinarily insured in Class 1, then his temporary boss must continue to see that his full flat-rate payments are kept going.

Responsibility for payment

In the first instance an employer is responsible for meeting the whole cost of such flat-rate contributions as are applicable to each of his men. But he may recover the employee's contribution, subject to the following conditions.

(a) He may deduct from the man's wages or other remuneration only the amount of the contribution due from him for the period for which the wages are paid. (b) He must not make deductions before paying the contributions. (There are exceptions to this, but they apply to large-scale enterprises employing at least 250 people, where flat-rate contributions may be made by cheque instead of stamps.) If the contributions are not paid until after he has paid the men's wages, an employer has no right to recover their share.

The employer must stamp the employee's insurance card for every contribution week during the whole or part of which the man is employed. If the man changes his job before midnight on Sunday, and his last boss has already seen to the stamping of his card, there is no liability on the new employer—unless, of course, the new job brings the employee into a different class.

Where a worker is insurably employed by two or more employers in the same contribution week, it is normally the first employer in the week who pays flat-rate contribution. But if the two regularly employ the same person they may agree, subject to the local Ministry people's approval, to take it in turns to pay.

As to holidays, the general rule is that the employer continues to pay flat-rate contributions for all or part of a week during which his employee is off. But where a man is away sick, no flat-rate contribution is due from his employer for any week, even a holiday week, during the whole of which the employee is incapacitated.

When contributions are payable

The basic rule is that the regular flat-rate contributions must be paid by stamping the employee's card not later than the time he is paid his wages. For weekly wage earners the card is stamped weekly, the monthly ones monthly. When the card expires, however, it must be stamped up to date within six days of the end of its run. And when a man's employment ends, his card must be stamped up to date straight away and handed over to him, even though his wages are not paid until later.

GRADUATED NATIONAL INSURANCE

The graduated pension scheme was introduced into national insurance in April, 1961. Previously retirement pensions were payable on a flat-rate basis only. The graduated scheme allows employees to qualify for additions to the basic pension on a rising scale related to their earnings and the corresponding contributions made on their behalf.

Like flat-rate insurance, the graduated scheme is fundamentally a compulsory one. It applies to employees aged 18 or over who earn over £9 in any week, and includes married women and widows whether or not they have chosen to pay flat-rate contributions; also unretired men between 65 and 70 and unretired women between 60 and 65 years of age.

Employees can be contracted out of the graduated scheme if their employment is covered by an adequate occupational pensions scheme.

In short, the general rule is that graduated contributions must be paid for all employees who (a) are in Class 1 for national insurance purposes, and (b) come under the normal arrangements for Pay As You Earn income tax.

The basis of contribution

Graduated pensions insurance applies to all earnings over £9 and up to £15 a week. At £15 the rate of contribution stays put, so that a man earning £20 pays no more than his colleague earning £15. The combination of pension contributions from the two sources brings therefore the following example liabilities:

Young John earns £8 a week. Only the flat-rate contribution is due.

The tractor driver earns £14. The flat-rate contribution covers the first £9; the balance of £5 attracts a graduated contribution.

The cowman earns £17. This requires a flat-rate contribution for the first £9, plus a graduated contribution on £6. The amount over £15 is disregarded.

To assist calculation, the Ministry of Pensions and National Insurance publishes tables of a ready-reckoner kind comparable to the income tax tables used in connection with Pay As You Earn. Indeed, contributions are calculated on the same figure of total pay as is taken for P.A.Y.E. But, unlike P.A.Y.E. in which the figures accumulate through the year, the amounts due are worked out according to each week's (or month's, etc.) wages taken separately. So that if in one week a regular employee receives

In which the figures accumulate throughout the year.

overtime, that is treated as part of his pay for that week, and an increased pension contribution becomes due.

Workers for different employers

Where an employee is doing two or more separate jobs under different employers, graduated contributions are calculated separately and independently on the wages paid by each. This rule applies whether or not each employer is actually deducting income tax from the wages. Where the pay exceeds £9 a week in each separate employment, this means that the employee is the subject of more than one graduated contribution for the week. As a result, if the employee's own graduated contributions in any one income tax year amount to £14 or more, a refund may be made to him. But no refund is available on account of the employers' contributions.

Part-time workers

Graduated contributions are not in general due on payments by an employer to an employee who normally does not do more than 8 hours' work a week for him. But if in any particular contribution week the employee does work more than 8 hours— so that, as explained earlier, a flat-rate contribution falls due for that week—a graduated contribution is due on the amount by which the week's pay exceeds £9 paid in any income tax week.

Where an employee who normally works more than 8 hours a week for the employer clocks up 4 hours or less in any particular contribution week, we have seen that no flat-rate contribution is due. Nevertheless, whatever he receives for that work must be included, in the usual way, in the total pay figure on which graduated contributions are calculated.

Calculation of gross pay

The sum on which graduated contributions are calculated is the " gross pay " as entered on the deduction card for P.A.Y.E. Among items included are wages, overtime, bonuses, pay continuing during absence for sickness, etc. Benefits in kind, such as free board and lodging on the employer's premises, are not added in.

Responsibility for payment

As with flat-rate insurance, the employer is responsible for paying both his employee's share and his own—which is an equal sum—but he is entitled to deduct the employee's contribution from the pay packet to which the contribution applies. Special deduction cards are provided for recording the employee's contributions, no note being made on them of the employer's share.

The employer must pay to the Collector of Taxes the total amount due in respect of his staff, both their share and his own, within 14 days of the end of each income tax month. For convenience he may send one cheque covering both graduated pension contributions and P.A.Y.E. tax deductions.

Chapter 16

SAFETY, HEALTH AND WELFARE

In 1956 Parliament embarked on a little by little campaign designed to give farm and forest workers the same sort of protection from occupational risks as their brothers in industry have long enjoyed. The foundation was the Agriculture (Safety, Health and Welfare Provisions) Act. This itself contains one or two shalls and shall-nots; otherwise it gives the Minister of Agriculture authority to build up the safety code by means of regulations as and when.

Since then the Minister has sponsored a number of Statutory Instruments compelling the farmer to watch his employees' steps, which we will take in order of appearance. But before that we should mention three matters comprised in the 1956 Act itself. Section 2 forbids " young persons "—those over compulsory school age and under 18—to carry loads of such weight that might do them an injury. Section 6 requires first aid boxes to be accessible to workers.

First aid boxes . . . accessible to workers.

Sections 3–5 give powers to sanitary authorities to see that sanitary facilities are provided and maintained. Where the authority consider that lavatory facilities are inadequate to the number and sex of the farm staff, they may serve notice to put the matter right. If the W.C.s are temporary or portable, the notice is served on the occupier. More permanent accommodation is, however, the landlord's responsibility, in which case the local authority serve notice requiring equipment on the landlord. Such a notice must give reasons why fixed equipment is necessary, against which the landlord has a right of appeal. Local authorities may also serve notices respecting the maintenance and cleanliness of existing lavatory accommodation.

For their further convenience, a farmer who employs workers must provide them with clean water, soap and clean towels.

First aid

Appropriately enough, this is the subject of the first of the regulations to supplement the 1956 Act. The Act itself says that the farmer must provide first aid facilities; the Agriculture (First Aid) Regulations, 1957 (S.I. 1957 No. 940) give a list of what dressings and medicaments must be kept in how many boxes. For example, a farm with one, two or three workers requires at least one small box or cupboard containing 3 finger dressings, 2 small and 2 medium plain wound dressings, 2 triangular bandages having a base not less than 51 in. long, 6 waterproof adhesive wound dressings, a half-ounce packet of cotton wool, and a copy of the official first aid leaflet, which is available free from the Ministry's local offices. Where the farm supports four or more workers, the requirements are correspondingly more in number, although medically of equal simplicity.

Ladders

The Agriculture (Ladders) Regulations, 1957 (S.I. 1957 No. 1385) forbid the use of other than well-made and well-maintained ladders. Employers must see that the ladders their workers use pass a number of tests. In particular, the grain of wooden stiles or rungs must run lengthwise; there must be no weakening defect visible in wooden stiles or rungs; rungs of a wooden-stiled ladder must not be supported entirely by nails or screws; wooden rungs must be fitted into stiles by rabbet, notch or mortice; tie-rods must be fitted not more than 2 ft. from each end of the ladder and not more than 8 ft. apart throughout its length—although this is not necessary if the rungs are through-tenoned and wedged in the stiles; steps or trestle ladders must be fitted with effective devices to prevent the back support from spreading; apart from trestle ladders, the distance between adjacent rungs must be no more than 12 in. centre to centre.

So much for construction. As to safe use, the regulations place responsibilities on both employer and worker, both of whom must make sure that a ladder is strong enough for its purpose; that no rungs are missing; that it is equally supported on each stile and securely placed or held in position; and that the top (except for steps or trestle ladders) extends above any point at which the worker has to get on or off it, unless there is some secure handhold available apart from the ladder itself.

If a farm worker finds any fault in a ladder he has to use, he must immediately tell his employer.

Power take-offs

The Agriculture (Power Take-off) Regulations, 1957 (S.I. 1957 No. 1386) are designed to protect the farm worker against harm from power take-offs and power take-off shafts on tractors and other machines. While the engine is in motion the power take-off must be covered by a shield, substantially constructed of metal or other material which is capable of supporting at least 250 lb. and which will protect a worker against contact from above or from either side. If, however, the power take-off is already sealed by a fixed cover, the shield is not required.

The power take-off shaft whilst in motion must be protected on all sides. Generally the protection must extend along its full length from the tractor to the first bearing on the machine; but there are two exceptions to this. First, if any part of the shaft's length is equally well protected by the machine itself, that portion need not be further covered by a guard. Secondly, if a machine already in use on 1st February, 1959, has a shaft which is 2 ft or less from the ground throughout its length, a guard in the form of an upside-down U will suffice, provided it extends at least 2 in. below the shaft on both sides.

Both employer and worker are responsible for complying with the power take-off regulations. A worker must not use a machine that does not conform; an employer must not cause or allow such a machine to be used.

Accidents to children

The next to appear, the Agriculture (Avoidance of Accidents to Children) Regulations, 1958 (S.I. 1958 No. 366) put a brake on joy-riding by children under 13 years of age. Pre-teenagers are forbidden to drive or ride on any tractors or self-propelled machines, or to drive self-propelled vehicles, while these are being used in, going to or coming from agricultural work. Nor must they ride on machines mounted on, or moved by tractors or vehicles; indeed they must not ride on binders or mowers even when they are drawn by horses.

They may ride on the floor of a mechanically drawn trailer, but if it is bearing a load they may ride on the load only if the trailer has four sides all higher than the load. They may not ride on any trailer which has a conveyor mechanism built in. Children may still, however, continue to ride on horse-drawn vehicles, such as wagons or haycarts.

Other possible sources of "give us a ride" which are barred to the under-thirteens include agricultural implements mounted on or moved by tractors or vehicles, rollers of all kinds whether drawn by horse or horse-power, also drawbars, etc.

Circular saws

The Agriculture (Circular Saws) Regulations, 1959 (S.I. 1959 No. 427) prescribe simple requirements for the less risky use of machinery "intended for sawing wood by means of a circular blade, exceeding 12 in. in diameter, in a fixed or portable bench frame". A farmer must not allow his workers, in course of their duties, to operate or assist at such a circular saw, unless it meets with these requirements:

It must be substantially constructed and properly maintained. There must be adequate light, artificial or natural. The blade must not knowingly be used if it is cracked, if it has been repaired by brazing or welding, if it has two or more teeth missing, or if it is warped or so otherwise out of true that its teeth make contact with the bench table when the blade revolves.

The saw must have a strong and rigid metal riving knife, with a smooth surface, set in a direct line behind the blade with the front edge extending upward and forward; this knife must be not more than ½ in. away from the teeth of the blade and must measure not less than half and not more than the total height of the blade above the bench table. The blade above the table must be protected by a rigid guard not less than one inch wide and kept as close to the blade as the work in hand allows; it must extend over the blade from above the riving knife at least far enough to be directly over the point where the cutting edge of the blade goes through the table; the part of this top guard extending beyond the top of the saw blade must either be parallel with the bench, or slope or curve downward. Below the bench the blade must be guarded by two plates of metal or other suitable material, one on each side; these plates must not be more than 6 in. apart and extend at least 2 in. beyond the circumference of the blade.

It is the worker's responsibility to keep in position and make every use of the riving knife, guard or other protection required by the circular saw regulations. If he finds certain defects in the saw which he is employed to operate, he must report them at once to his employer. These include cracks in blades, two or more missing teeth, teeth that come into contact with the bench when the saw is revolving, and damaged or missing rives or guards. The fact that the worker must report such defects does not lessen the employer's obligations.

Then there are several responsibilities shared jointly by master and man. Three concern general working conditions. Thus, the floor or ground area used by a worker operating a circular saw must be unobstructed and give a firm foothold. Whenever it reduces the risk of injury, a wooden push-stick or push-block must be used at a saw fed by hand. No adjustment must be made to the saw or its guards while the blade is rotating, except to devices which regulate the rate of feed or the depth, width or angle at which the wood is cut.

The other regulations which affect both employer and employed provide that a worker who has never operated a circular saw shall not do so until the way it works has been demonstrated by someone over 18 years of age who has a thorough working knowledge of that kind of saw. No worker under 16 may operate or assist at a circular saw, and one between 16 and 18 may only operate under the supervision of an expert of 18 or over. Finally, no worker is allowed to operate or assist at a circular saw until someone has explained the regulations affecting him.

Safeguarding of workplaces

The Agriculture (Safeguarding of Workplaces) Regulations, 1959, (S.I. 1959 No. 428) deal with precautions in places where farm workers are employed; they principally concern stairs, floors and walls.

First, as to stairways—and a stairway is a permanent staircase or a permanently fixed ladder, either inside a building or giving access to it. No step may be fixed solely by nails, screws or similar devices. No stairway may have any step missing or any other weakening and visible defect. All staircases which reach 3 ft. or more above ground must have at least one handrail; if there is an open side it must be on that side, if two open sides there must be a handrail on each. Handrails must be of suitable material, such as wood or metal, strong, smooth, rigid and securely fixed; and they must run the whole length of the stairs, except where a part would obstruct access.

Stairs so steep that they amount to fixed ladders do not need fixed handrails, but they must have a secure handhold for the worker to use at the top, e.g., a short extension of one of the stiles.

Next, the workplaces rules give attention to openings through which a worker might tumble and injure himself. Those through or from which he might fall more than 5 ft. must be guarded—by fences not less than 3 ft. high, or by rails between 3 and 3½ ft. above the floor, or by covers. Openings in floors must be guarded by a cover, fence or guard-rail. Edges of floors must be guarded by fence or guard-rail, other than where the floor ends at an opening in a wall. Openings in a wall of a building must be guarded by a door, fence or guard-rail; though this does not apply to openings 4 ft. or less from top to bottom, or to those with sills more than 2 ft. above the floor.

Such covers and guards must be strong, firmly fixed and properly maintained. They must be kept in place, except for the limited time when they need to be removed for the movement of people and materials, during which time a handhold must be available, unless the cover is a self-closing trap door. Rails must be fixed either directly above the edges of the opening or, provided there is an intermediate rail between $1\frac{1}{2}$ and $1\frac{3}{4}$ ft. above the floor, they may be up to 10 in. outside the vertical. Where an opening gives access to a stairway, these provisions about guards do not apply.

There are similar rules aimed at making safe grain pits, stokeholds and furnace pits into which a worker might fall more than 5 ft. Their openings, too, must be guarded by covers, fences or rails of the kind specified above. But in their case handholds are not legally required when the guards are removed, and the rails must be directly above the edge of the opening, whether or not there is an intermediate rail.

The prime responsibility for safeguarding workplaces in the regulation style is the employer. But if the employer is not the farm occupier—if, for example, he is a contractor whose men happen to be on the farm to unload fertilisers or do relief milking—then the occupier is liable.

Employees have their share of responsibility. They must not open or remove any cover, door, fence or guard-rail except for such necessary purposes as moving material about. The farmer's own workers must report to him any missing or broken step in any stairway they have to use, also broken handrails, covers, fences or guard-rails.

Stationary machinery

The Agriculture (Stationary Machinery) Regulations, 1959 (S.I. 1959 No. 1216) apply to machinery and prime movers of a fixed nature, as distinct from such sources of power as movable threshers or balers. A "stationary machine" is one adapted for stationary use only; but the term does not include threshers, hullers, balers and trussers, which are the subject of special regulations considered later. "Prime movers" includes not only those that would fall into the definition of "stationary machine" but any other internal combustion engine or electric motor, whether or not designed for stationary use only, used to drive stationary machines.

Components of stationary machines, i.e., shafting, pulleys, flywheels, gearing, sprockets, chains, belts, and fans and their wings and blades, must be guarded so that they protect a worker from contact with them, unless they are so positioned that he is safe against contact—that is to say, where they are more than $6\frac{1}{2}$ ft. from places to which he has access. Any chains or belts moving at less than 30 ft. per minute, and all conveyor chains or belts, need only be guarded at their run-on points.

Primary driving belts—i.e., those that transmit power from the prime mover—which form part of a permanently fixed installation must be guarded along their whole length. Others need to be guarded merely at their run-on points. But here again exceptions are made in the case of belts working at least 6 ft. 6 in. out of harm's way.

Feeding inlets and discharge outlets of grain augers, and of power-driven machines which grind, crush, bruise or pulverise grain, must be guarded so as to protect workers against contact with moving parts of the augers or with internal moving parts of the machines. Similarly, feeding inlets and discharge outlets of power-driven machines which cut or pulp roots, chop hay or straw, or grind, break, mix or pulverise feedingstuffs require guards to protect workers against contact with internal working parts.

There is no " standard " type of guard prescribed for all these precautions: but whatever the design it must be adequately strong and properly maintained.

Then there are regulations about stopping devices. Every prime mover must have a readily accessible contrivance, such as a switch, by which it may quickly be stopped. It must be placed on or near the prime mover, unless the latter is more than $6\frac{1}{2}$ ft. from places to which a worker has access or is otherwise so situated as to prevent the worker coming in contact with it. Every stationary machine, other than a prime mover, must be fitted with a loose pulley and striking gear, or with a clutch or other device, readily accessible to the operator of the machine, by which the power transmitted from the prime mover may be quickly disconnected. But this is not needed if the prime mover's stopping device is readily accessible to the operator of the machine.

Where any worker dresses or handles products near moving parts, the means of disconnecting the power must be within his reach from his working position; or, at any rate, from one of them when a group is in action there. If such a machine has several stages where workers handle produce, these considerations apply to each stage.

Certain special precautions apply to switches. Thus there must be a clear indication at every prime mover's switch how the thing may be stopped, and each switch must be clearly identified with the prime mover it belongs to. Where two or more switches control a prime mover, or a stationary machine with a built-in mover, they must be so connected that once the power is cut off at any one switch, it cannot be reconnected unless that one switch is subsequently operated by hand.

It almost goes without saying that belts and their fastenings have to be properly maintained; and no belt may rest or ride on a revolving shaft. Also, where any machine or prime mover is in use there must be adequate natural or artificial light.

Compliance with the stationary machinery regulations is primarily the employer's burden. He must not cause or permit a worker to use any prescribed machinery unless the above requirements have been satisfied. Employees are required to make full use of the guards and facilities installed, and they must keep guards in place except when cleaning, repairing or adjusting machines at a standstill, or when making essential adjustments to moving machines that cannot be carried out otherwise. The temporary removal of guards from prime movers is also allowed where it is necessary for the manual starting of the motor. But none of this work may be done by workers under 16. Finally, an employee is obliged to report damaged guards to his employer.

Heavy weights

In order, no doubt, to give the farmer time to use up his traditionally-sized sacks, the Agriculture (Lifting of Heavy Weights) Regulations, 1959 (S.I. 1959 No. 2120) do not come into operation until 1st July, 1965. From that date, the maximum weight of any sack which a farm worker may lift or carry unaided shall be 180 lb. This does not, of course, affect section 2 of the 1956 Act, to which we referred early in this chapter, whereby no young person employed in agriculture shall lift, carry or move a load which may cause him injury by its weight.

Threshers and balers

The Agriculture (Threshers and Balers) Regulations, 1960 (S.I. 1960 No. 1199) contain safety requirements for *stationary* threshers, hullers, balers and trussers—those which are made or permanently converted for stationary use only. They do not affect viners or combine harvesters, even when temporarily used for threshing.

Perhaps the most important requirements are to do with guards, for which there is no specification other than that they must be strong, well maintained and adequate to protect workers against dangerous parts of machinery. When produce is being fed into the drum of a thresher, the feeding mouth must be guarded in such a way that a worker is protected against contact with the drum; this is unnecessary, though, with threshers fitted with self-feeders which incorporate the same degree of protection. When the drum is rotating without being fed, the feeding mouth must be covered so as to make it impossible for the worker to come in contact.

The deck of a thresher from which a worker might fall more than 5 ft. must be fitted with guards at both ends and on the side not being used for the movement of produce. Such guards—whether rail, rope, chain or fence—must be from 3 to 4 ft. above the deck, and supported by uprights not more than 8 ft. apart. Every baler must be fitted at both sides with a guard to protect workers coming into contact with the ram; every trusser requires a guard to give protection against the discharge arms.

Other parts of threshers and balers which must be so situated or guarded as to offer no danger from contact include shafting, pulleys, flywheels, gearing, cranks, sprockets, belts and chains. In the case of a primary driving belt between a prime mover and a thresher or baler which are not permanently fixed in relation to each other, similarly in the case of a belt or chain connecting a thresher and baler, only the run-on points need to be guarded. Where a thresher or baler is *permanently* fixed in one position, any components which are more than $6\frac{1}{2}$ ft. from places to which a worker has access in course of his employment would be regarded as safely situated and need not be guarded.

The regulations also compel the provisions of means by which threshers and balers may be quickly stopped. They may comprise either (a) a readily accessible device, such as a switch, fitted on the prime mover, or (b) a device fitted on the thresher or baler to disconnect it from its prime mover. Whichever device is used, it must be constructed and maintained so that the power cannot be reconnected except by hand, foot or other bodily means. And if any prime mover is controlled by more than one switch, they must be connected in such a way that if the power is disconnected at one switch, the same switch will have to be manually operated again before the prime mover can be restarted.

All belts and their fastenings have to be well maintained; no belt may rest or ride directly on a revolving shaft. Wherever a prime mover or machine is used there must be adequate light. Finally, pointed hooks and spikes must not be used to attach a sack or bag to a thresher. It may be taken that hooks and spikes are satisfactorily unpointed if they are no sharper than a match head.

As with other safety measures. the responsibility for carrying out the stationary threshers and balers regulations is divided. Fundamentally the burden rests on the employer. If threshing or baling is done by a contractor, whether a machine is owned, hired or borrowed by him, he is the "employer" for the purposes of the regulations. In every other case the employer is the occupier of the farm on which threshing or baling is taking place.

The worker's main responsibility is to keep in position and make full use of all guards provided under the regulations. Guards may be removed from threshers and balers in use only for so long as it is necessary to carry out any essential adjustments which cannot be made unless the machine is running. They may be removed from machines which are not running for so long as is necessary for repairs or adjustments. A worker under 16 years of age may not remove a guard. A worker must report damaged guards to his employer, whether occupier or contractor.

Concerning joint responsibilities, while a thresher drum is rotating no worker may stand on any platform or other surface which slopes down directly into the feeding mouth. No worker may be on top of a baler while it is operating. And no worker under 18 may feed produce into the drum feeding mouth of a thresher.

Compliance with the law

The safety laws, then, contain much to digest, and it would require a superhuman memory to commit all their details to heart. Nevertheless there they are, to be read, marked, learnt and acted upon. The penalty for defiance is laid down in the 1956 Act with which this chapter began. A person guilty of an offence is liable, on summary conviction, to a fine not exceeding £50.

It is given to inspectors of the Ministry of Agriculture, to enter farms and interview the boss and his workers, without notice, at any reasonable time; although 24 hours' notice must be given if they wish to enter a dwelling-house. While employer and employed must generally reply to the inspectors' questions, they need not answer those which might incriminate themselves.

PART IV

THE FARMER AND THE GUILDHALL

In this part we give a general account of local authorities and other public bodies and their powers and duties. Naturally we give particular attention to those powers and duties which affect agricultural land. Powers of land acquisition are dealt with in connection with each of the various purposes for which land or interests in land may be acquired compulsorily. At the end of this part we refer to the Town and Country Planning legislation as applied to agricultural land and buildings.

Chapter 17

LOCAL AUTHORITIES

Local authorities as we know them today are the indirect descendants of the old overseers and guardians of the poor but over the last two centuries they have assumed a wide variety of functions which have brought them ever more closely into contact with the everyday lives of ordinary people. Local authorities in this sense are all of them composed of Councils elected on the familiar democratic principle and responsible for administration in a fixed geographical area. There is a good deal of overlapping as to territorial limits but the boundaries for local government

A wide variety of functions.

purposes are subject to periodic review by the Local Government Boundary Commission. They may conveniently be classified in five groups:
- (a) County Councils;
- (b) County District Councils (i.e., Urban and Rural District Councils);
- (c) County Borough Councils;
- (d) Borough Councils; and
- (e) Parish Councils.

Broadly speaking County Councils are responsible for the admini-

129

stration of police, education and highways in their area and have overriding authority in matters of town and country planning. County District Councils, which may be either urban or rural, are primarily responsible for housing, public health and sanitation in their areas; they also exercise a delegated authority in town and country planning matters. County Borough Councils (i.e., the larger towns) exercise the powers of county councils within their boundaries but they also exercise the powers of county district councils or virtually all local government powers. We are not particularly concerned in this book with Borough Councils but they exercise most local government powers with the exception of police and education. The functions of Parish Councils are virtually confined to the provision of simple amenities, such as parish halls.

Nearly all the major functions, which we have listed above—education, highways, housing, sanitation and water supplies, public health including sewerage, and the protection or diversion of footpaths—may involve the acquisition of agricultural land or may affect the use of adjoining agricultural land and we deal with these matters in detail in the ensuing chapters. We must also deal with certain other public bodies which, though they are equipped with statutory powers and responsibilities, are not local government authorities. Some of these, like the River Boards and the Water Boards, are composed largely of members nominated by local authorities in certain fixed proportions. Others, like the British Transport Commission and the Gas and Electricity Boards, are nationalised industries. Their local subsidiaries are not directly responsible to the local government.

Private rights and public powers

Just how does the individual stand in relation to his local authority in cases of dispute? For example, you live in a rural district council area. The Public Health Act, 1936, says that rural district councils are to be responsible for the provision of adequate sewerage in their areas, but the public sewer comes to an end a mile down the road and your house is drained into a septic tank. To some extent the language used in the statute which imposes the duty upon the authority may answer this question differently in different cases. It may be that the local authority is under a specific duty to do what is wanted or it may have a mere power to do so. Many parliamentary hours have been consumed in discussion as to the relative advantages of the words " may " or " shall " in statutes. In the case of sewers, however, the local authority are certainly under a duty, but the duty is general in character and not sufficiently precise to enable individuals to compel the authority to act in particular cases.

Far more difficult legal questions arise where a local authority in the course of exercising its statutory powers exercises them in such a way as to damage the property of a private citizen. In general " statutory authority " is a defence to an action based upon this kind of conduct, unless the local authority have been negligent. In other words, if the damage suffered by the individual is an inevitable consequence of the exercise of their powers by the authority the individual will have no redress. A case in point is *Metropolitan Asylum District v. Hill,* 1881, where the authority in pursuance of their powers erected a fever hospital on land adjacent to Mr. Hill's land. The court held that because *some* damage would have been inevitable wherever the fever hospital had been placed, the plaintiff could not be heard to complain of the nuisance arising from it. This does not mean, however, that statutory authorities may avail themselves of their statutory powers so as to do their work regardless of the comfort or interests of private people. If they do their work negligently in such a way as to occasion loss or damage then they will be liable. An example of a case of this sort was *Jones v. Mersey River Board,* 1957, in which the Court of Appeal held that the River Board would be liable for damage caused by spreading spoil on the land adjacent to a river. The dividing line between these two sorts of case is a difficult one to define, but we do not think it is unduly difficult under modern law to succeed with an action for damages against a local authority on grounds of nuisance or negligence, provided that there has been avoidable physical damage to land.

Until 1954 local authorities were to some extent protected by the Public Authorities Protection Act, 1893. This required that no action should be brought in tort against a local authority unless the writ were served within six months of the act or acts complained of. This short limitation period, however, was extended by the Law Reform (Limitation of Actions) Act, 1954, and the period for actions against local authorities is now six years, or three years in the case of an action involving personal injuries.

Chapter 18

COMPULSORY PURCHASE AND COMPENSATION

Valuation for compulsory purchase, as for any other purpose, is obviously a highly intricate business calling for specialised practical knowledge, but the underlying principles to be applied are principles of law based on common sense and ordinary fairness which may be readily understood. In the 18th century when land was acquired for public purposes the compensation provisions were

A highly intricate business.

usually written into the statute which provided the necessary powers (generally a local or private Act) in each particular case. Differing provisions led to disparities in the compensation awarded, and in the early 19th century Parliament became concerned about these difficulties and passed a series of general measures, the Lands Clauses Acts, which were eventually consolidated in one statute, the Lands Clauses Consolidation Act, 1845. This laid down the fundamental rules of compensation which still remain effective today. Clearly the underlying purpose of compensation, namely to place the disappropriated owner of property in something approximating to the position he would have enjoyed had it been unnecessary for his property to be acquired, needs a good deal of amplification in practice. Just what interests in land, for example, would call for the payment of compensation should they be

133

acquired and just what effects of compulsory purchase in the case
of, say, roadbuilding would the landowner be entitled to be compensated for? The Act of 1845 laid down three basic principles
which have guided the courts in answering these questions. It
provided that compensation should be payable for:—

(a) the value of the interest acquired;

(b) loss suffered by reason of severance or " injurious affection "
to the lands held with the land acquired; and

(c) losses suffered by way of disturbance.

We shall now have to deal with these separately to see just what
losses are involved under each heading.

(a) *The value of the interest acquired.* This means the value
of the interest to the owner himself or, in general, what he could
sell his interest for in a voluntary deal. Later legislation made
considerable inroads upon the provisions of the 1845 Act relating
to the interest in the land, but the only one we need mention is
that which governs the position of tenants from year to year. This
is to be found in section 121 of the Act which provides that such
tenants are to be compensated for the value of their interest at the
date of acquisition. Thus, to take a practical illustration, a tenant
under an annual tenancy of an agricultural holding is entitled to
certain tenure for twelve months plus the unexpired portion of the
current year of his tenancy. Accordingly if his interest were
acquired or cut short during the currency of a year of his tenancy
he would be entitled to compensation based on his loss of profits
for this period. The value of the interest to be acquired is, of
course, a matter of common sense in each case. Thus, a free-
holder would be entitled to freehold value, a leaseholder would be
entitled to the value of the unexpired term of the lease and so
forth.

(b) *Severance and injurious affection.* Compensation under
this heading in connection with lands held with the land acquired
is perhaps the most difficult part of the exercise. Developments
like motorways, trunk roads and railways involve serious damage
from being cut up, or "severed", and in many cases the compensation under this head may exceed the compensation for the value of
the actual land acquired. From the decided cases it is reasonably
clear that the calculation under this head must be based (in the
case of a farm) upon the increased cost of running the holding
resulting from the severance capitalised over a reasonable period—
say 20 years.

(c) *Disturbance.* Compensation for " disturbance " in this
context means something much wider than disturbance under the
Agricultural Holdings Act, 1948, which we have already seen at
page 42, is strictly limited to the loss or expense incurred by

the tenant and directly attributable to the sale or removal of household goods, livestock and equipment. The Act of 1845 by contrast does not define disturbance at all and it has been left to the courts in a series of decisions to decide upon the scope of compensation under this head. In fact it has been held at various times to cover a long list of items including business losses arising from the removal from one business address to another, the expenses involved in the physical process of removal and the expenses incurred in searching for alternative accommodation even when this has proved unsuccessful. The last item has been held to include legal costs and surveyors' fees (see *L.C.C.* v. *Tobin,* 1959).

After 1845 the law of compensation was largely allowed to take its course for nearly a century. Values were based on open market prices, but a rule of practice arose whereby it became customary to award an extra 10 per cent to the landowner over and above market value as a " sop " to console him for the compulsory nature of the sale. After the first world war Parliament decided to overhaul the provisions governing the assessment of compensation and it was then laid down that this procedure should not be adopted in future. In the Acquisition of Land (Assessment of Compensation) Act, 1919, six new rules for the assessment of compensation were introduced. These are now re-enacted in section 5 of the Land Compensation Act, 1961, which deserves to be quoted in full: —

" Compensation in respect of any compulsory acquisition shall be assessed in accordance with the following rules:

(1) No allowance shall be made on account of the acquisition being compulsory:

(2) The value of land shall, subject as hereinafter provided be taken to be the amount which the land if sold in the open market by a willing seller might be expected to realise:

(3) The special suitability or adaptability of the land for any purpose shall not be taken into account if that purpose is a purpose to which it could be applied only in pursuance of statutory powers, or for which there is no market apart from the special needs of a particular purchaser or the requirements of any authority possessing compulsory purchase powers:

(4) Where the value of the land is increased by reason of the use thereof or of any premises thereon in a manner which could be restrained by any court, or is contrary to law, or is detrimental to the health of the occupants of the premises or to the public health, the amount of that increase shall not be taken into account:

(5) Where land is, and but for the compulsory acquisition would continue to be, devoted to a purpose of such a nature that there is no general demand or market for land for that purpose, the compensation may, if the Lands Tribunal is satisfied that reinstatement in some other place is bona fide intended, be assessed on the basis of the reasonable cost of equivalent reinstatement:

(6) The provisions of rule (2) shall not affect the assessment of compensation for disturbance or any other matter not directly based on the value of the land."

Subject to what follows, these six rules have become the basic precepts governing the assessment of compensation. Rule 5 dealing with "equivalent reinstatement" is couched in discretionary terms. It is intended primarily to deal with land and buildings (like churches or chapels) used for some purpose which does not of itself attract any ascertainable market value. Where the "equivalent reinstatement" principle applies the practical result may frequently be a much higher rate of compensation.

Procedure

The procedure to be followed by the acquiring authority is apt to vary according to the purpose for which land is to be acquired. Such general rules as exist, however, are laid down in the Acquisition of Land (Authorisation Procedure) Act, 1946. Briefly the Act provides that where a statutory authority proposes to acquire land in pursuance of its powers, the authority may make a compulsory purchase order. Notice must be given to owners and certain occupiers affected and the order must be published in local newspapers. A period must then be allowed for objections, after which the authority must submit the order for confirmation to the central government department responsible. Thus, for example, a compulsory purchase order for the acquisition of land for building a school would be submitted for confirmation to the Minister of Education. The Minister may or may not confirm the order after holding a Public Inquiry if necessary. After confirmation of the order there is a period of six weeks within which persons aggrieved by the order may apply to the High Court if it appears that the formalities have not been duly complied with. The High Court, in such cases, has jurisdiction to quash the order but only on grounds of want of formality or if the authority appears to have exceeded its powers. There is no jurisdiction to quash such an order on grounds of policy. There is also an expedited procedure which may be used in certain approved cases, but this procedure again is subject to rights of appeal.

After confirmation of the order the next step is for the authority to serve upon the owners and those occupiers whose interests are to be acquired by compulsory powers, a formal notice called

" a notice to treat ". The date of this notice is important because it is upon this date that the property must be valued for compensation purposes. Suppose, for example, that Coldcomfort Farm is to be acquired by the local authority for a sewage works. Notice to treat was served in October 1961. Thus if the farm was worth £15,000 as a going concern in 1961 but the local authority do not complete the purchase until 1966, any increase or decrease in the value of the farm which takes place in the meantime will be discounted.

Compensation becomes payable by the authority at the date of entry upon the premises. "Notice of entry" may be given at any time after notice to treat, even though there may be questions of compensation still to be settled. In the event of the authority entering before the settlement of compensation questions, the sum finally agreed or ordered to be paid in compensation will relate back to the date of entry, and interest upon the final sum will be payable from that date at the rate (usually 1 per cent above bank rate) prescribed from time to time by Treasury regulations.

The effect of planning control

Until 1947 compensation for the value of the interest acquired had always been based on the open market value of the property, which, in the case of land ripe for development, very often included a substantial premium over and above the ruling price for agricultural land as such. The effect of the Town and Country Planning Act, 1947, however, by imposing a general control over all development, was substantially to transfer this premium or " development value ", as it was called, from private individuals to the state. Owners whose land was ripe for development in 1947 were given a statutory right to claim upon a three hundred million pound fund —the fund to be fed by development charges levied upon all development for which planning permission had been granted. This ingenious system proved extremely difficult in administration and in 1952 the Government partially repealed these provisions. Development charges were abandoned and no further claims on the three hundred million pound fund were to be entertained (though established claims were kept alive for the purposes of compulsory acquisition).

This resulted in practice in two distinct levels for land prices. If land were sold for development in the open market (planning permission having been granted for private development) it would obviously realise its true value as a site for the particular development contemplated. If, however, the same land were acquired under a compulsory purchase order for similar development, the combined effect of the Town and Country Planning Acts, 1947–54 was that compensation for the value of the interest acquired would consist of:—

(a) the value of the land in its existing use, plus

(b) the amount of an established claim on the three hundred million pound fund, if any.

In practice the compensation awarded on this basis frequently bore little resemblance to the open market value of the property and in many cases serious hardship resulted. Land with no substantial development value in 1947 might have acquired considerable development value by, say, 1955. Perhaps the point is best illustrated by an example. Let us assume that A, a market gardener, bought a six-acre holding on the outskirts of a new suburb in 1950. Its value as a market garden (and let us assume for the sake of argument that this figure remains constant at all times) is £6,000. In 1947 the site had virtually no attractions for developers and accordingly no claim was made and the property therefore, to use the stilted language of the 1954 Act, had no " unexpended balance of established development value ". By 1950, however, the property had become fairly attractive in view of advancing development in the area and consequently A had to pay £10,000 to secure it. In 1956 the local authority decided that the place would make an ideal site for a school and a compulsory purchase order was duly made. In the meantime A had received attractive offers from private developers but to his surprise found that these would not be acceptable as evidence of value. In effect his compensation was limited to its existing use value in 1956 (there being no claim under the 1947 Act) namely £6,000.

The Town and Country Planning Act, 1959

This state of affairs was very considerably ameliorated by the Act of 1959. It has sometimes been said that the 1959 Act restored the basis of compensation to the open market value standard. This is substantially true, though it is really an oversimplification. The Act certainly reintroduced open market value as the basic standard but this time it is open market value *within the limits of permitted development*. As a solution to the problem this obviously has the merit of being realistic. Planning control is something with which we have lived since 1947, and its practical effects upon market values simply cannot be ignored. There are two main provisions of the 1959 Act with regard to compensation. The first is that if the purpose for which land is to be compulsorily acquired has an ascertainable market value (e.g., for local authority housing) then the compensation payable must not be less than the price which the land would command if it were to be developed privately as a site for that purpose (e.g., land required for local authority housing = not less than housing site value to a private developer). The second main provision of the Act is that the compensation payable must not be less than the value of the land for any private use for which planning permission might reasonably have been expected to be given. Thus if, say, a nursery garden in a residential area is to be acquired for some public purpose without ascertainable market value and it is reasonable to expect that planning permission would have been forthcoming for private housing, then the compensation payable shall not be less than housing site value to a private developer.

The Act contains provisions for ascertaining the planning position of any particular site. If no planning permissions have already been granted the owner may apply to the planning authority for what is called a Certificate of Alternative Permitted Development. The planning authority must then say what uses they would have permitted if application had been made to develop the land privately. If the owner is not satisfied with the certificate granted, or if a certificate is refused, he has a right of appeal to the Minister of Housing and Local Government. In practice the system is not free from difficulty where the acquiring authority and the planning authority are one and the same, but the right of appeal to the Minister is a certain safeguard in such cases.

The various compulsory purchase provisions of the 1959 Act, and those of the 1947 Act remaining in force, were consolidated in the Land Compensation Act, 1961.

Special protection for tenant farmers

Finally there is one further provision of the 1959 Act of special interest in agriculture. This is section 37 which does not strictly apply to compulsory purchase cases but for convenience may be dealt with here. The section provides that where an applicant for planning permission is the owner of the land in question he must inform leaseholders *and* in the case of agricultural land yearly tenants in possession. Where the applicant for planning permission is not the owner of the land in question he must inform the owner and the other two classes of people just mentioned. It will be seen that these provisions do help to clear up an old difficulty. Before the 1959 Act it frequently happened in the case of agricultural land that the tenant had no knowledge of the application to develop until he received a notice to quit under section 24 (2) (b) of the Agricultural Holdings Act, 1948, referring to the fact that the land was required for a use for which planning permission had been granted. Under the 1959 Act, however, he has an opportunity to make representations to the planning authority before any decision is taken.

The position of occupiers

Unfortunately many local authorities and other public bodies do not have to comply with the ordinary planning procedure and so when a proposal for compulsory purchase is made, it frequently happens, even after the 1959 Act, that the occupier's first knowledge of the proposal takes the form of a notice to quit or to resume possession of part of the holding under the Agricultural Holdings Act, 1948. In the case of tenanted farm land there are two possible procedures which the acquiring authority may follow. First they may use their compulsory powers both to acquire the freehold and to cut short the tenant's interest. The tenant's position, if this course is adopted, has been outlined earlier in this chapter (at page 134). Alternatively the authority (and this is by far the commoner practice) may purchase the freehold, either by compulsory powers or by agreement, and then, standing in the landlord's shoes, proceed to determine the tenancy of all or part of the land by any means available to them either under the tenancy agreement or under the Act of 1948. We have already seen in Part I (at page 38) that the tenant may be served with an unchallengeable notice to quit under section 24 (2) (b) where the land is required for a purpose other than agriculture for which planning permission has been granted or is not required. The notice given by the local authority must therefore comply with this section and it must contain a clear statement of the purpose for which the land is required and a reference to planning permission either having been granted or not being required. In general if this procedure is adopted the tenant will be entitled to 12 months' notice, whether the notice relates to all or part of the holding, and his compensation will be exactly the same as that which would have been his due if notice had been given for some permitted non-agricultural use by his original landlord.

The authority may be able to take possession at less than 12 months' notice provided that the tenancy agreement contains a "resumption clause". In other words, if the landlord originally reserved the right to resume possession at less than 12 months' notice for specified non-agricultural purposes, the authority will be able to take advantage of this clause. Here the notice given must be for a reasonable period (see *Coates v. Diment*, 1951) to give the tenant an opportunity to serve necessary notices relating to compensation.

Finally the local authority must take care not to fall foul of the provisions of section 31 of the 1948 Act in the case of a notice to quit part of the holding. This provision again has already been discussed at page 41, where we saw that notices to quit part of a holding are void at common law. The effect of section 31 is to validate such notices provided that they are given for certain specified purposes. The purposes specified there are fairly wide and include most of the objects for which a local authority might want to develop land. If, however, the purpose is one for which section 31 does not permit a notice to quit part of the holding, the local authority would have no alternative but to make a compulsory purchase order to acquire the tenant's interest, which would involve the payment of compensation on the (higher) loss of profits basis.

The settlement of claims

Under the Act of 1919 a system of official arbitration was established for the settlement of claims for compensation in the event of land being compulsorily acquired. This continued until the establishment of the Lands Tribunal under the Lands Tribunal Act, 1949, when this function was passed to the new tribunal. The Lands Tribunal (not to be confused with the Agricultural Land Tribunals) is therefore in effect the " court of appeal " for compensation cases.

In general the procedure is that upon service of notice to treat the owner has 30 days within which to negotiate with the district valuer, who will in practice make the first offer, subject to negotiation. If there appears to be no prospect of reaching agreement the owner may then at any time give written notice to the district valuer that he intends to appeal to the Lands Tribunal. The Lands Tribunal will then in due course hold a hearing and make its decision. There is a further right of appeal, but on points of law only, to the Court of Appeal.

Cases of hardship

In recent years it has become increasingly apparent that, where possession of a farm or some substantial part of a farm has to be given up, the compensation provided under the Agricultural Holdings Act, 1948, is by no means adequate to compensate the tenant for his actual loss. In the prevailing conditions of scarcity of farm land, reinstatement in another farm may be impossible or at best extremely expensive, and the equivalent of two years' rent plus tenant right and compensation for improvements can scarcely be regarded as adequate in these circumstances. In two cases in recent years special provision has therefore been made in local statutes to alleviate the hardship which may be involved by the provision of special compensation in the discretion of the acquiring authority. The first example of this is to be found in the Liverpool Corporation Act, 1957, which provided for the acquisition of land in the Treweryn Valley for the making of a reservoir. The second example is the Tees Valley Water Act, 1960, under which land was to be acquired for the construction of a reservoir at the head of the River Balder. In each case the payment of compensation under these local provisions is discretionary and the decision of the acquiring authority is final. It may be that this practice of making special provision for cases of hardship in local statutes will become general, but under present law there is no general enactment providing for such payments.

Chapter 19

HIGHWAYS AND FOOTPATHS

HIGHWAYS

A highway has been described as " a defined strip of land over which the public as a whole and without distinction have a right of passing and repassing ".   Any land, in other words, over which the public enjoy a right of way is a highway, even though the right of way may be limited or subject to conditions.   For example, certain classes of traffic are excluded from the use of motorways, which are none the less highways within the wide definition of that term just quoted.   A public footpath is technically a highway but in this chapter we shall deal with footpaths separately because in relation to agricultural land they stand in a very different position from all other highways.

Creation of highways

Traditionally there are three ways in which a highway may be created.   They are:

(a) by dedication (which simply means that the owner of the land has dedicated it or declared his intention that it be used as a public highway by means of express or implied grant);

(b) by prescription or long user (prescriptive rights are considered in relation to nuisance in Part V—see page 185); or

(c) by statute.

In modern times the third method of creating highways, i.e., by statute, is by far the most important.   Nearly all new public roads are created in this way, usually by the highway authority acting under general powers or special powers conferred by a local Act of Parliament.   Public rights of way may, however, on occasion be acquired by prescription, but such rights of way are more often claimed than granted.

Prescription is really a form of legal presumption based upon evidence of use.   Thus where it can be shown that the public have exercised " de facto " use of a path or road for a substantial period without hindrance from the owner of the land, the law will presume that the owner or his predecessor intended to make a grant.   But the use must be of a definite character.   The alleged rights must have been exercised openly.   They must not have been exercised by force or with a show of force and, of course, they must not have been exercised subject to any kind of permis-

sion. The Rights of Way Act, 1932, laid down that 20 years
should be sufficient to raise the presumption of dedication but this
presumption could still be rebutted by evidence inconsistent with
an intention upon the part of the landowner to dedicate land as
a highway. The provisions of the Act of 1932 were incorporated
in the Highways Act, 1959.

Preventing rights of way

" How can I prevent the public acquiring rights of way over
my land? " is a common question. Merely to close the path or
road, which would obviously be effective, is not always a practicable
answer. Some landowners follow the practice of closing the road
periodically, say, for one day in each year, because to establish
prescriptive rights the user must have been continuous and without
interruption. Sometimes it may be convenient as an alternative
to display a notice disclaiming any intention to dedicate. Such
notices are frequently seen in the countryside and usually refer
to the Rights of Way Act, 1932. Notices put up for this purpose
after 1959 should strictly refer to the Highways Act, 1959. The
precise wording is immaterial but some such formula as the following may be useful:

> " The public may use this path/road at all reasonable times
> by permission of the owner. The permission hereby granted
> may be cancelled without notice."

There is one statutory method whereby owners of land may
protect their title against the acquisition of public rights of way.
The owner may make a simple statement defining the path by
reference to a plan and denying any intention to dedicate to public
use. This statutory declaration must be deposited with the County
Council in their capacity as the authority responsible for highways
and footpaths.

Motorways and trunk roads

Modern traffic calls for not only faster roads but safer roads,
and provision was made in the Special Roads Act, 1949 (Motorways) and in the Trunk Roads Act, 1946, for the creation of
two new classes of highway. These differ from conventional highways in two respects. In the case of trunk roads there are strict
limits upon points of access to the road. In the case of motorways
access is limited to vehicles entering or leaving from major roads
at fixed points; there is also a restriction upon the classes of
vehicle which may use the road.

Where motorways or trunk roads pass through agricultural land,
then quite apart from compensation problems, which have been
dealt with in Chapter 18, there may well be difficulties about
fencing or drainage. Both of these involve factors which depend

upon locality and must be worked out by negotiation at the time of acquisition. The Minister of Transport (in the case of motorways) or the County Council (in the case of trunk roads) is under a general obligation to make the road safe for traffic. There are, however, no specific obligations as to fencing. In practice the authorities will undertake to provide stock-proof fencing and will make themselves responsible for its maintenance. In the event of livestock escaping on to a trunk road or motorway the position appears to be the same as in the case of any other highway, subject to any special conditions which may have been agreed between the owner of the land and the highway authority. In the case of motorways district valuers accept responsibility for fencing on the Minister's behalf.

Maintenance and repair

Historically the function of maintenance belonged to the inhabitants-at-large of the district. The inhabitants could be indicted at common law for failure to keep highways in repair, but they might be acquitted if they could show that the adjoining landowner was responsible either by custom or by reason of his tenure. In modern times the County Councils, in their capacity as highway authority, are the successors, in this sense, of the inhabitants-at-large. Theirs is the general duty to keep highways in repair and to keep them safe. They will be liable to road users if damage results from some negligent act on their part (but in general not for damage resulting from mere omissions). Most of their powers are now statutory and specific. In the course of maintenance they may make roadside ditches to secure adequate drainage of the highway and, where a roadside ditch was originally dug in these circumstances, the highway authority became responsible for its maintenance. Many such ditches perform a dual purpose by receiving the surface run-off from the highway and also the water percolating through field drains from the adjoining land. Where this is so the highway authority may require the occupier of the adjoining land to keep the ditch in order if its condition creates a nuisance (see section 130 of the Highways Act, 1959). Similarly the authority may require occupiers to lop overhanging trees or shrubs where these constitute a danger to traffic. Alternatively the authority may do the necessary work and recover the reasonable cost from the occupier (see section 134 of the 1959 Act).

Certain acts known as highway nuisances are prohibited by the general law. For example, it is a public nuisance to discharge a firearm within 50 ft. of a highway to the annoyance of passers by. Some highway nuisances, for example, allowing the highway to become fouled by sewage are continuing in character, and the highway authority may take steps to abate the nuisance and claim the reasonable cost from the occupier.

Apart from nuisances which are prohibited under the general law, certain acts may be prohibited by byelaws made by the County Council and subject to a confirmation procedure. Many counties have now adopted a byelaw making it an offence to deposit mud from vehicles upon the surface of the highway.

Road charges

One of the recognised perils involved in buying property adjacent to an unmade road is the risk that at some future date the local authority may seek to pave the road and charge the occupiers of adjoining land. This procedure is not to be used for highways for which repairs are a charge on the general rate, but it may well be used for unmade service roads accommodating a group of houses or farms, and this may involve considerable expense upon the frontagers. The power of a local authority to deal with a private road in this way originated in the Private Street Works Act, 1892 (which was incorporated in the Highways Act, 1959). A local authority may resolve to " sewer, level, pave, metal, flag, channel or make good, or provide means of lighting " for any street not being a highway repairable by the inhabitants-at-large which needs this work to be done. The authority may apportion the cost among the frontagers either according to frontage or according to benefit. A right of appeal to the Magistrates' Court is available if the frontager is aggrieved by the apportionment, but the magistrates can only consider the fairness of the apportionment as between the frontagers. In other words, if the authority have based the apportionment upon frontage, the magistrates cannot make a new apportionment on the basis of benefit.

FOOTPATHS

The law relating to footpaths was considerably clarified and brought up to date by Part IV of the National Parks and Access to the Countryside Act, 1949, which was substantially re-enacted in the Highways Act, 1959. The Act provided for a footpath survey to be conducted by County Councils throughout the country to ascertain the position and direction of all paths which were subject to a public right of way. The survey was to be performed in three stages, allowing time for objections or for local inquiries, if necessary, to confirm or otherwise the existence of a public right of way. The survey was to culminate in the publication by the County Council of a final map marking all established footpaths in the county. Most County Councils have now reached this final stage and the maps are available for inspection at County Council offices. The map should show if the right of way is subject to any restriction—i.e., if the path is a footpath only or is a bridle path.

Maintenance

The maintenance of footpaths is often a source of difficulty. Usually it is not economic for the County Council to pave them, even if this were desirable. The repair of stiles, gates and bridges, however, along the path may be the responsibility of the highway authority or of the landowner according to the circumstances. Section 38 of the 1959 Act preserves the landowner's obligation to repair by reason of his tenure where this obligation exists at common law, and if in such a case the footpath authority carry out repairs on, say, a bridge, they may recover the reasonable cost or a proportion of the cost from the landowner. It is sometimes said that the cost of repairs should be apportioned according to benefit (i.e., the expense should be borne by the local authority *in so far as the repairs contribute to the enjoyment of the footpath as a footpath*). Some of the decided cases seem to lean towards this view, but we do not find it an easy rule to apply in practice.

Ploughing up

Subject to restoration, farmers have certain fixed rights to plough up footpaths which interfere with agriculture. By section 119 of the Highways Act, 1959, if a footpath or bridleway crosses agricultural land and it is convenient in the interests of good husbandry when ploughing the land to plough up the footpath also, then the occupier may plough the path provided he gives at least seven days' written notice to the highway authority. This is, however, subject to the further proviso that he must " as soon as may " be after the end of ploughing make good the surface of the

To plough up footpaths which interfere with agriculture.

path so as to make it reasonably convenient for the exercise of the public right of way. Failure to give advance notice is an offence punishable with a fine of up to £2 and failure to restore is an offence punishable with a fine of up to £10 plus £1 a day after conviction for as long as the offence continues. One or two recent cases before the magistrates have illustrated the difficulties resulting from the use of the rather vague words " as soon as may be ". On one occasion this was held to mean at the end of ploughing and on another occasion it was held to be sufficient if the footpath was restored after harvest or " at the end of the series of agricultural operations" of which ploughing formed part. There is no decision of the High Court directly in point and so for the time being at least we think farmers would be well advised to do exactly what the Act says !

Stiles and gates

In certain circumstances occupiers may apply to the footpath authority for permission to erect stiles or gates where these are reasonably necessary for agriculture. In practice permission is fairly readily granted and appeal lies upon the refusal of permission to the Minister of Housing and Local Government. As regards diversion or stopping up of footpaths it is extremely rare for a footpath to be stopped up on agricultural grounds. Occasionally, however, permission is given for a path to be diverted (e.g., around a poultry farm in order to reduce the risk of disease). Here again there is a right of appeal to the Minister.

Duty to footpath users

Broadly speaking the occupiers of farms owe no special duty to the users of footpaths. This, however, must be read subject to one or two exceptions. Section 143 of the Highways Act, 1959, makes it an offence to use barbed wire fences adjoining a public path, if this may result in danger to users of the path. The authority may require the occupier to remove the wire or may do the work themselves and recover the cost. There is also a general power to make byelaws prohibiting the keeping of bulls in fields where public paths run, and such byelaws have been made by several County Councils.

Chapter 20

WAYLEAVES

A wayleave is a legal right to bring a substance over, under, through or across land.

In this chapter we discuss some of the main purposes for which the various local authorities and statutory bodies may acquire the right to bring cables or pipelines through agricultural land. In recent years we have had several instances in the courts illustrating

The right to bring cables or pipelines through agricultural land.

the serious effects which development, such as electricity cables carried on pylons, may have upon farming operations and consequently upon the capital value of farms affected. The legal difficulties involved in wayleaves are considerable, and because there appears to be no standard procedure we deal separately with the various purposes for which wayleaves may be acquired.

Sewers and water mains

Under section 15 of the Public Health Act, 1936, public health authorities were given powers to lay sewers or water mains through agricultural land, subject to reasonable notice and the payment of compensation. As regards the laying of sewers, these powers are now exercisable generally by urban or rural district councils as public health authorities. As to the laying of water mains the powers originally granted to public health authorities are now exercisable by the local water undertaking.

The compensation provisions are exactly the same in each case and are to be found in section 278 of the Act of 1936 which provides:—

"(1) Subject to the provisions of this section, a local authority shall make full compensation to any person who has sustained damage by reason of the exercise by the authority of any of their powers under this Act in relation to a matter as to which he has not himself been in default.

(2) Any dispute arising under this section as to the fact of damage, or as to the amount of compensation, shall be determined by arbitration:

Provided that, if the compensation claimed does not exceed fifty pounds, all questions as to the fact of damage, liability to pay compensation and the amount of compensation may on the application of either party be determined by, and any compensation awarded may be recovered before, a court of summary jurisdiction.

(3) No person shall be entitled by virtue of this section to claim compensation on the ground that a local authority have in the exercise of their powers under this Act declared any sewer or sewage disposal works, whether belonging to him or not, to be vested in them, or on the ground that he has sustained damage by reason of any action of a local authority in respect of which the authority are by this Act authorised to pay compensation if they think fit.

(4) Where an owner of land claims compensation in respect of damage sustained by reason of a local authority having, in the exercise of their powers under this Act, constructed a sewer or laid a water main in, on or over his land, the tribunal determining the amount of the compensation shall determine also by what amount, if any, the value to the claimant of any land belonging to him has been enhanced by the construction of the sewer or the laying of the water main, and the local authority shall be entitled to set off that amount against the amount of any compensation awarded."

We have given the full text because the section is by no means an easy one to interpret, and there has been a good deal of argument between farmers and local authorities as to its meaning. Some local authorities claim that the duty under subsection (1) to "make full compensation to any person who has sustained damage" is fulfilled merely by paying for the physical damage to the land in the course of construction. It has been held, however, in *Thurrock Grays and Tilbury Joint Sewerage Board v. Thames*

Land Company Limited, 1925, that the wayleave for a water main or sewer is an easement or right in or over land and as such is within the definition of "land" in the Acquisition of Land (Assessment of Compensation) Act, 1919 (now section 39 of the Land Compensation Act, 1961). Quite apart from merely carrying out works the authority are acquiring certain rights over the land including the right to re-enter for maintenance or repair and (even more vital) their right under section 25 of the Act of 1936 to prevent development which would be likely to interfere with their right of access to the sewer or water main. Accordingly the Thurrock Grays case laid down that the principles applying to the assessment of compensation are exactly the same as those which, as we have already seen in Chapter 18, apply to the acquisition of all "interests in land". It will be remembered that compensation falls to be assessed under three heads:—

(a) the value of the interest acquired;

(b) injurious affection to or severance of other land; and

(c) disturbance.

The value of the interest acquired is more difficult in the case of a wayleave than in the case of outright acquisition, but some attempt must be made to arrive at a figure and this is usually done by taking half the agricultural value of the strip of land on either side of the line in respect of which development is likely to be disallowed. Where land has actual development value, the claim for this part of the loss should be made under (b), while the compensation for disturbance is limited in practice to physical damage to land or crops.

The procedure is simply that applicable to outright acquisition with one or two modifications. First it is necessary for the claimant to serve a notice of claim upon the Council under section 4 of the Land Compensation Act, 1961. The section provides that the notice "must state the exact nature of the interest in respect of which compensation is claimed and give details of the compensation claimed, distinguishing the amounts under separate heads and showing how the amount under each head was calculated . . ." If after 30 days from the receipt of such notice, the Council has failed to make an offer or the parties have failed to reach agreement, the owner may refer the question of compensation to the Lands Tribunal for settlement.

Two points remain to be dealt with. One is that in cases where the claim is for £50 or less either party may refer the question of compensation to the Magistrates' Court in preference to the Lands Tribunal. The other is the provision for the setting off of what may be called "betterment" under section 278 (4) of the Public Health Act, 1936. Where a water main is laid there may well be some resulting enhancement to the value of the property as a whole and in practice the claim for compensation may be considerably reduced in such cases. The same would apply in the case of a sewer if the value of the property as a whole were to be enhanced by the laying of the sewer.

Electricity wayleaves

Wayleaves for electricity cables and pylons present perhaps the most difficult problem from the point of view of compensation. Although everyone accepts the development of the national electricity grid as being desirable in itself, there is frequently no advantage to the affected farm when the pylons make their appearance and consequently there is usually no question of " betterment " to be offset against damage and inconvenience. In the case of these wayleaves the position is governed by section 22 of the Electricity Supply Act, 1919. The powers conferred by the section are now exercisable by electricity boards, subject to the consent of the Minister of Power. Owners or occupiers may object to the order and the Minister may hold a local Public Inquiry before making up his mind as to the merits of the proposal. No express provision is made for compensation, but the Minister may confirm the order upon " such terms and conditions " as he thinks fit, and in practice the orders usually contain provision for compensation which takes the form of an annual wayleave payment. In order to secure uniformity over the country the Central Electricity Generating Board makes announcements from time to time about the wayleave rentals which it considers appropriate for the various types of land. These announcements are made after consultation with interested bodies. Such " agreed " rentals are not intended to be binding upon the Boards or upon the owners of land affected. They are intended merely as a guide and as a basis for negotiations in each case.

Government pipelines

A number of long distance Government oil pipelines were laid during the war under emergency powers. This involved the use of requisitioning procedure and compensation was payable under the Compensation (Defence) Act, 1939. Under the Act of 1939, which was intended to apply to all land requisitioned for purposes of the emergency, owners were entitled to a rental compensation for the duration of hostilities plus a capital sum at the date of derequisitioning intended to represent the depreciation (if any) in the capital value of the land between requisitioning and the date of handing back to the original owners. In practice these principles did not work well as applied to pipelines and Parliament made proper provision for Government pipelines in the Land Powers (Defence) Act, 1958.

The procedure for making orders as to pipelines is laid down in Schedule II of the Act. The Minister must first prepare a draft order showing the proposed route of the pipeline by reference to a map and this draft order must then be served upon " every owner, lessee or occupier of any of the affected land " (the only exception being tenants for a month or any period less than a month). If objections are made and not withdrawn, the Minister must give the objector an opportunity to be heard by " a person appointed by the Lord Chancellor to hold an inquiry " but the hearing may be held in private. For the purpose of dealing with objections, the Minister may disregard an objection if he is satisfied that it relates " exclusively to matters of compensation ". After considering the objections the Minister may confirm the order with or without modifications and once again notices must be served upon the owners and occupiers affected. Thereafter " any person aggrieved by the order " has a right to apply within six weeks to the High Court and the Court may set the order aside if they find that the formalities have not been properly complied with. This is rather wider than the right to apply to the High Court under the Acquisition of Land (Authorisation Procedure) Act, 1946, which can be invoked only by owners *and certain occupiers*. The right under the Act of 1946 could not be invoked by a tenant from year to year of an agricultural holding.

Section 16 of the Act deals with the protection of the oil pipeline in the ground; and certain uses of the land once the line has been laid are prohibited. The section applies to the land immediately above the pipeline and extending for 10 ft. on either side of the line. In this area it is forbidden, without the consent of the Minister, to place any building or structure, or to build any road or hard standing, or to carry out any excavation, or deposit any " earth, refuse, spoil or other materials ".

It is not intended, however, that the section should prevent ordinary agricultural operations such as ploughing or grazing. In the case of agriculture there are only two types of operation which would be illegal without the Minister's consent and these are:

(a) the storage of crops, grass or silage; and

(b) mole drainage.

Compensation is dealt with in section 18. The owner of any interest in the affected land may claim an amount " equal to the amount of depreciation " of the value of his interest, and disputes about the amount of compensation are to be determined by the Lands Tribunal. The procedure and time limits for making claims to compensation are governed by Treasury regulations—the Government Oil Pipelines (No. 2) Regulations, 1959 (S.I. No. 724).

Commercial pipelines

In recent years the high cost of transport has driven some of the major oil and chemical companies to resort increasingly to the use of long-distance pipelines for the conveyance of oil, gases and liquid chemicals. The companies concerned felt that these projects, which are regarded as highly desirable in the national interest, required statutory powers, and in several cases between 1955 and 1962 Private Bills were promoted in Parliament for this purpose. In each case guarantees were given by the promoters during the passage of the Bills through Parliament as to compensation, protection of crops and stock, drainage and temporary fencing. The four pipelines constructed under special powers are the South Wales Pipeline (petrol and oil), the Shell (Stanlow to Partington) Pipeline (polyethylene), the Esso (Fawley, Hampshire, to London Airport) Pipeline (petrol) and the Esso (Fawley to Severnside) Pipeline (petrol).

In 1962, in view of the feeling that commercial development of this type should not be compelled to run the gauntlet of the somewhat difficult and hazardous procedure involved in promoting private legislation in Parliament, the Government introduced general proposals for a uniform procedure under the control of the Minister of Power. The Pipelines Act, 1962,* enables the Minister to regulate, in the interests of safety, the construction, operation and maintenance of both cross-country and local pipelines. The pipeline is defined as a pipe or system of pipes conveying anything other than air, water, water vapour or steam, but not including drains, sewers, pipes for domestic purposes, or for heating or cooling, or for conveying materials on building sites. The definition includes ancillary apparatus, such as pumps.

The Act provides that pipelines more than 10 miles long (cross-country pipelines) may not be constructed without the "pipeline construction authorisation" of the Minister. The applicant is required to advertise the project, and provision is made for the hearing of objections and for the holding of a Public Inquiry. Pipelines not exceeding 10 miles in length are called local pipelines; they may be constructed without the express authorisation of the Minister. However, the Minister must be given 16 weeks' notice of the laying of such a pipeline to enable him to give directions in the interests of safety. Planning permission for local pipelines remains the responsibility of local planning authorities.

As regards the compulsory acquisition of land or rights in land, the settlement of claims for compensation is governed by the Land Compensation Act, 1961, and the Lands Tribunal Act, 1949. As in the case of Government oil pipelines, the Minister may make orders to protect the pipeline from surface encroachments within 10 feet in order to maintain free access to the land for maintenance and repairs. There is a general obligation upon pipeline owners so far as is practicable to restore agricultural land so as to be reasonably fit for use.

---

* At the time of publication, the Pipelines Bill, 1962, is before Parliament and is expected to receive the Royal assent during the present session.

Chapter 21

DRAINAGE AND SEWERAGE

In this chapter we deal first with the main provisions for securing the adequate drainage of agricultural land and then with the main provisions dealing with the disposal of domestic and farm sewage. We have placed these two subjects together because of their

Provisions for securing the adequate drainage of agricultural land.

obvious points of similarity though they are usually treated quite separately in the text-books on local government. In both these fields farmers are brought into contact with public bodies exercising statutory powers—with river boards in the case of land drainage and with district councils in the case of sewage. There is also the vital question of river pollution which is of common interest to both sets of authorities.

Improved land drainage has recently been described as the most urgent need of the land in many parts of Britain. The neglect of two world wars and the break-up of many of the larger rural estates have doubtless contributed handsomely to present difficulties. The system of grants for drainage improvement which has operated since the war is simply not enough without some provision for the control and co-ordination of individual drainage schemes within a catchment area. And only in 1961 were the river boards given new powers to deal with the parlous state of the so-called " intermediate watercourses ". By contrast sewage is something of a new subject for farmers. The domestic variety, in which sanitary authorities may show greater or less interest according to inclination, has been under their supervision since 1936. However, fashions in husbandry are apt to change and one of the side effects of the modern vogue for intensive units of production has been the considerable problem of how to deal with the excess manure which cannot be absorbed into the ordinary agricultural operations on the land. Broilers, deep-litter poultry, cattle fattening in covered yards and pigs housed on the sardine principle, tend to produce an *embarass de richesse* which received Parliamentary recognition as " farm effluent " in the Public Health Act, 1961.

LAND DRAINAGE

River Boards and land drainage

The parent of modern land drainage is the Land Drainage Act, 1930. The Act carved up much of England and Wales into catchment areas, each embracing a main river or group of rivers with their tributaries bounded by the watershed. In 1948, under the River Boards Act, the newly constituted river boards and the river conservancies for the Thames and the Lee took over all the existing functions of catchment boards with the addition of certain navigation functions. The drainage powers of river boards therefore arise directly under the Act of 1930. Under the Act the drainage powers of the board apply only to rivers which the board has designated as " main rivers ". The amount of river so designated depends inevitably upon the financial resources available to do work which the board regards as necessary, which may include the dredging or deepening of rivers or streams, the widening or straightening of rivers and generally keeping the rivers in a proper state to do their drainage work effectively. The boards are composed predominantly of members nominated by the various county and county borough councils in their respective areas, whose task it is to allocate the funds available for the various works in order of priority.

The boards are financed by means of " precepts " (i.e., levies) on the county and county borough rates at so much in the pound of rateable value. In areas of special drainage needs like Lincolnshire, for example, the precept may be four or five times as high as in natural free drainage areas. This revenue from local rates may be to some extent supplemented by central government grants, but these can be discounted in practice except for major improvement schemes.

Internal Drainage Districts

In areas of special drainage difficulty within the larger catchment area of a river board, there is provision in the Act of 1930 for the establishment of what are called "internal drainage districts". Such internal drainage districts may be administered directly by the board itself or, where this is more convenient, an internal drainage board may be established for the purpose. There is power to levy a drainage rate upon the area "deriving benefit or avoiding danger" from works within the district, and in practice this has been treated, since 1933, as including all the land up to a level of 8 ft. above the top flood level of the watercourse in question. Thus under the Act of 1930 drainage rates have been and continue to be payable in respect of such land at so much in the pound of gross Schedule A value. The primary obligation to pay such rates is divided between owners and occupiers according to the board's declaration as to the proportion of its expenditure which has been attributable to capital works and maintenance respectively during the rating period. Owners are primarily responsible for capital works and occupiers for maintenance, but it is open to the parties to a tenancy agreement to provide for the whole amount to be paid by either landlord or tenant. There are detailed provisions in the Act for financial adjustments as between the main board and the internal drainage board, if any.

The Land Drainage Act, 1961

It will be seen that apart from major schemes on main rivers and a patchwork of internal drainage districts scattered over the country, the 1930–1948 Acts left large areas quite untouched. "Intermediate watercourses" was the name given to the remaining streams which were neither—

(a) part of the main river so designated by the river board; or

(b) part of an internal drainage district.

Such watercourses might vary in size enormously from healthy rivers at the upper extreme down to something little more exciting than a farm ditch at the other end of the scale. It is with these watercourses that the Land Drainage Act, 1961, is primarily concerned. The Act empowers river boards, *within their discretion,* to levy a charge for the purpose of financing works upon these watercourses upon all agricultural land and buildings in their area outside internal drainage districts. This general charge is limited to the equivalent of the level of the precept in the particular river board area concerned. This involves a rather difficult calculation, because the precept is based on rateable value while the general charge must be in terms of Schedule A. On present figures a precept of 3d. in the pound on the rates is probably equivalent to a charge of about 4½d. in the pound on Schedule A. It should be noted that the board's power to make the general charge is discretionary, and doubtless there will be many areas where the administrative costs of collection would be considered to exceed the practical advantages of bringing this part of the Act into operation.

Under the Act of 1961 there is a further power to make a special charge over and above the general charge in "areas of special agricultural need". This involves the board in submitting a scheme to the Minister, and there are opportunities for objections and the holding of a Public Inquiry. The scheme, if approved, may be financed by the levying of a further charge which may bring the total charge to a figure not exceeding 1s. in the pound of Schedule A value (including the special agricultural charge, if any).

Duties of the boards

In general the duties of river boards are permissive, not compulsory, in character; consequently they will not be liable for the results of flooding or any other damage caused by their failure to carry out their statutory functions. There is a procedure under section 22 of the River Boards Act, 1948, which gives a right of complaint to the Minister, who may hold a Public Inquiry and give directions to the board to carry out specified work if he thinks fit. There is also provision in section 34 of the Land Drainage Act, 1930, which *empowers* a board to pay compensation where damage is caused to land in the course of dredging, widening or other operations; but there is no positive right to compensation under this section, which is purely discretionary. Apart from these provisions the position is governed by the general principles of common law, which have already been discussed in relation to public bodies generally where damage is caused in the course of work carried out under statutory powers. In general the board will be liable only for damage caused by some positive negligent act carried out by or on behalf of the board. The board will not be liable for damage which would have been an inevitable consequence of the exercise of its powers (see *Marriage v. East Norfolk Catchment Board*, 1949). It would appear, however, that once the board have taken positive action and carried out works in relation to any stretch of river, they then become subject to a general duty of care in the carrying out and maintenance of their schemes. For example, if the board had installed a system of sluices and their servant then negligently failed to open a sluice in time to prevent flooding, the board would be liable for the resulting damage. Also it has been held that where a natural watercourse is replaced with an artificial watercourse under statutory powers, the responsible body will be liable for the resulting damage if their substituted watercourse proves inadequate and will not be able to escape liability by a defence based on "Act of God", even in the case of exceptional rainfall. (This is the effect of a decision in *Greenock v. Caledonian Railway*, 1917).

Deposit of spoil

A common cause of complaint against the activities of the boards is the spreading of spoil from dredging operations on the adjoining land, which, although on occasion it may be beneficial, may frequently be harmful. Before 1961 there was some doubt about their precise rights in depositing spoil and section 34 of the Act of 1930, which dealt with the power of the boards to pay compensation in certain cases, did not appear to provide adequately for the case where land was damaged by the deposit of spoil. The difficulties were illustrated in *Jones v. Mersey River Board,* 1957, where the Court of Appeal held that the Board's right to deposit spoil without paying compensation was limited to the " banks " of the river. This was found to be a difficult rule in practice, as it gave no real guidance to the extent of the banks, and the difficulties were to some extent cleared up by section 29 of the Act of 1961. This provides that the boards may deposit spoil on the banks of the watercourse extending to the width that would be needed for the spoil to be removed from the watercourse and deposited in one operation by machinery. If the deposit of spoil causes damage which could have been avoided with reasonable care the board will be liable to pay compensation. In addition the board has power to pay compensation on an *ex gratia* basis, even where the damage could not reasonably have been avoided.

Neighbourly disputes

The boards have certain limited powers of compelling occupiers to take action where rivers or streams are silted up or otherwise obstructed. These were extended by the Land Drainage Act, 1961, and may be used by certain other authorities in addition to river boards. Under section 28 of the 1961 Act, any river board, internal drainage board, county council or county district council can serve notice requiring an obstructed watercourse to be put in order. The notice can be served on the person in control of the watercourse, or the person who has caused the obstruction, or the owner or occupier of adjoining land. The notice must specify the work required together with a time limit. If the notice is not complied with in time the authority may do the work themselves and recover the reasonable cost from the person concerned, who may also be liable for a £5 fine. There is a right of appeal against the notice to the Magistrates' Court.

A common difficulty arises where A's land is flooded as a result of B's failure to keep his ditch in a reasonable condition. Quite apart from the ordinary principles of nuisance (and the statutory powers just mentioned) there is a summary remedy appropriate for use in a situation of this kind. This is provided by section 45 of the Act of 1961, which lays down that where the land is being injured, or where its drainage cannot be improved because a neighbour neglects his ditches, the owner or occupier of the affected land may apply to the Agricultural Land Tribunal which may, after hearing both sides, make an Order requiring drainage work to be carried out within a period of not less than three months. The Tribunal has power to call for a technical report from the Ministry of Agriculture and if the Tribunal's Order is not complied with the Ministry of Agriculture can arrange to have the work done and recover the reasonable cost from the person named in the Order. Application to the Tribunal is made on Forms 12 or 14, which have already been mentioned in Chapter 8 where we dealt with the various functions of Agricultural Land Tribunals.

The battle against pollution

The general law as to pollution is contained in the Rivers (Prevention of Pollution) Act, 1951. The river boards are given a general responsibility to detect and prevent pollution and by section 2 it is an offence to cause or knowingly permit any " poisonous, noxious, or polluting matter " to enter any stream. The boards also have an unusual power to apply to the County Court for an order prohibiting a proposed use of a stream when a breach of the section is anticipated. Under section 5 the river boards have wide byelaw making powers for the purpose of prohibiting various uses of rivers and streams which might lead to pollution, and for determining when matter is to be treated as poisonous, noxious or polluting. Some river boards have already had byelaws confirmed under the section prohibiting various uses including, for example, the washing of agricultural machinery in streams. Finally the consent of the river board is necessary in advance before bringing into use any new or altered outlet for the discharge of trade or sewage effluent into a stream. The board may give their consent subject to conditions, and if they do so the conditions will be binding on the successors of the person making the application.

SEWERAGE

Domestic sewage

Every public health authority is under a general obligation to provide for the sewage needs of its district under the Public Health Act, 1936. In fact by virtue of the Act every owner or occupier of premises has a positive right to connect and discharge into a public sewer vested in the local authority. In practice the right to do so may be of little value where there is no public sewerage scheme within easy reach, because the owner or occupier would have to pay the lion's share of the cost of connection. The great majority of rural properties discharge sewage into cesspits or septic tanks and the local authority has no powers in respect of these unless they are allowed to cause a public nuisance.

In certain circumstances, however, the local authority may actually require owners or occupiers to have their premises connected to the public sewer. In practice the local authority's right to insist on a connection is limited to cases where:—

(a) the public sewer is not more than a hundred feet from the site of the building; and

(b) no special difficulties arise from different levels or rights to cross intervening land.

These are the only circumstances in which the local authority may insist on the occupier connecting to the sewer at his own expense. If the authority want to make a connection in cases where these circumstances do not apply they must themselves pay the extra cost.

Farm sewage

As we mentioned at the beginning of the chapter, "farm sewage" is something of a modern phenomenon. Until 1961 the public health authority had no power to deal with it and no express power to make charges for so doing. Parliament, however, in the Public Health Act, 1961, placed farm effluent in exactly the same position as "trade effluent" which is regulated by the Public Health (Drainage of Trade Premises) Act, 1937. The combined effect of the Acts is to give a limited right to discharge farm sewage into the public sewers. Local authorities may make byelaws governing the times of discharge and the character of permitted effluents.

The local authority have power to make charges for the reception and disposal of trade effluents generally. If they fail to reach agreement with the occupier as to the amount of the charges there is a right of appeal to the Minister.

It should be noted that in general there is no absolute right to discharge farm effluent into the public sewer. In cases where a discharge was made by agreement with the local authority before the coming into operation of the Public Health Act, 1961, express consent will not be necessary. But where a new discharge is to be made, however, the consent of the public health authority is required, and obviously this consent will be subject to conditions as to charges.

Chapter 22

TOWN AND COUNTRY PLANNING

Perhaps the most important functions of local authorities from the point of view of farmers are those concerned with the control of development and land use generally. These functions have been acquired mostly under post-war legislation and are generally classified under the comprehensive and indeed provocative title— Town and Country Planning. Various attempts at planning new development in towns and at restricting ribbon development along

Various attempts at planning.

principal highways had been made in pre-war years, but after the second world war Parliament decided that nothing short of comprehensive control over building and all other development throughout the country would suffice to contain the enthusiasm of developers in the anticipated scramble for good building land.

Control of development

The Town and Country Planning Act, 1947, has already been mentioned in outline in Chapter 18 in connection with compulsory purchase. The Act itself is lengthy but the general scheme is simple. First a general embargo was placed upon all development as defined without permission. Detailed control was to be exercised by county councils who were to prepare development plans for the whole of their areas. A Ministry of Town and Country Planning was established and the Minister was to exercise general control in two principal ways. He was empowered: —

(a) to act as a " court of appeal " from decisions of local planning authorities; and

(b) to make regulations granting wholesale or "blanket" planning permission for certain prescribed developments.

One of the most difficult tasks of the legislature was to define development and the definition is to be found in section 12 of the Act of 1947, where it is defined very widely as " the carrying out of building, engineering, mining or other operations in, on, over or under land or the making of any material change in the use of land or premises." The definition is reasonably plain apart from the use of the words " material change of use ". A number of cases have turned upon these words and it has been held, for example, in *Eastbourne Corporation v. Fortes Ice Cream Parlour*, 1959, that to instal a milk vending machine outside a milk bar does not involve a material change of use. In other words, for the change of use to be material it must be substantial. It has been held that a mere intensification of an existing use will not amount to development so that, for example, a mere increase in retail sales of, say, eggs or chickens from a farmhouse or fruit and vegetables from a market garden, would not in itself involve development.

" Blanket " permission for agricultural uses

In 1949 the Ministry of Town and Country Planning was dissolved and its powers taken over by the Ministry of Housing and Local Government. In 1950 the Minister made a General Development Order exercising his power mentioned under (b) above to give blanket planning permission for certain developments. One of the classes of development for which blanket permission was thus granted was agricultural buildings other than dwelling houses. A good deal may turn on this, and the relevant words in Class VI of Part I of the First Schedule to the Order deserve to be quoted in full:—

" 1. The carrying out on agricultural land having an area of more than one acre and comprised in an agricultural unit of building or engineering operations requisite for the use of that land for the purposes of agriculture, other than the placing on land of structures not designed for those purposes or the provision and alteration of dwellings.

2. The erection or construction and the maintenance, improvement or other alteration of roadside stands for milk churns, except where they would abut on any trunk or classified road.

3. The winning and working, on land held or occupied with land used for the purposes of agriculture, of any minerals reasonably required for the purposes of that use, including the fertilisation of the land so used and the maintenance, improvement or alteration of buildings or works thereon which are occupied or used for the purposes aforesaid ".

The permission granted under this provision which would apply to all ordinary farm buildings and other farming developments in areas not subject to a specially strict degree of control are subject to two overriding qualifications. Both of these apply to buildings or other developments above ground level, and the effect of them is that the deemed planning permission shall not apply to developments:—

(a) within 80 ft. of the metalled part of a trunk or classified road or developments likely to affect visibility at a road junction; or

(b) development involving the laying out or material widening of the means of access to a trunk or classified road.

In each of these cases express permission must be sought from the planning authority which will, in the case of applications involving questions of road safety, automatically consult the Ministry of Transport Divisional Road Engineer before making its decision. Applicants have the usual right of appeal to the Minister in the event of refusal of permission, and the right of appeal may be exercised if planning permission has not been granted within three months.

The larger agricultural buildings

As we have seen the blanket permission granted for agricultural buildings is very wide and general in its effects. It is, however, subject to the Minister's right to make further regulations and also subject to the Minister's right under Article 4 of the 1950 Order to approve directions made by local authorities and relating to specific areas which revoke in whole or in part any of the different permissions granted under the Order. Article 4 provides that the Minister, if satisfied that there are convincing reasons on grounds of good planning in any particular area for requiring that developers should seek express permission for any particular development, may make a special order modifying the provisions of the General Development Order. Directions under Article 4 were extensively used to control the erection of broiler houses in Surrey and elsewhere in the Home Counties.

A patchwork of directions under Article 4 is, from the point of view of the authorities, by no means a satisfactory method of controlling large scale agricultural developments and in 1960 the Minister after consultation with interested bodies made a new

General Development Order—The Town and Country Planning General Development (Amendment) Order, 1960, (S.I. 1960 No. 283) requiring that:—

" The ground area covered by any building erected pursuant to the permission in the 1950 Order shall not, either by itself or after the addition thereto of the ground area covered by any existing building or buildings (other than a dwelling house) within the same unit erected or in course of erection within the preceding two years and wholly or partly within 100 yards of the nearest part of the said building, exceed 5,000 sq. ft."

This means that express planning permission will be required in every case for such developments.

One point should be noted, and this is that a direction under Article 4 of the 1950 Order is in effect a revocation of an existing planning permission. Section 21 of the Town and Country Planning Act, 1947, requires that where an existing planning permission is revoked the developer may make a claim for compensation if he has already incurred expense on the strength of the planning permission which had earlier been granted. Such claims were made effectively in several of the broiler cases, where broiler houses already under construction had to be dismantled in view of directions under Article 4 and subsequent refusal of planning permission.

Where angels fear to tread

There are certain sacred areas of the country where such a high degree of protection is thought to be required that all agricultural buildings (regardless of size) are regarded with suspicion. These are the National Parks and certain other places like the Quantock Hills and the Gower Peninsula in which the seal of official approval has been set upon the work of nature by designation as " areas of outstanding natural beauty ". These areas are governed by Special Development Orders which make them curiously unattractive to speculative developers. In general, written notice of all intended development (including agricultural buildings) must be given to the planning authority. If, within 14 days, the authority reply requesting a formal application for permission, the " developer " must comply with this and permission, if granted, will no doubt be subject to strict conditions about siting, colour and design.

Protection of agricultural land

When the planning legislation became fully effective it was thought that special protection would be needed for land currently in use for food production. This was achieved administratively by the Ministry of Town and Country Planning by directing planning authorities to consult the Ministry of Agriculture in all planning applications affecting agricultural land. The planning authority would then in effect be bound to follow the advice of the Ministry of Agriculture's Regional Land Commissioner as to the quality of land affected and its importance for food production. It was found in practice that this process of consultation consumed a great deal of time for the Land Commissioner and his staff, and in 1958 the Ministry of Housing and Local Government gave new instructions that this procedure should apply only for sites of five acres or more.

" Openness, fairness and impartiality "

Two considerable improvements in the planning procedure were introduced on the recommendation of the Committee under Sir Oliver Franks which reported in 1958 on Tribunals and Inquiries. The first of these has been mentioned in the chapter dealing with compensation at page 139 but applies equally to all planning applications. This is the rule under section 37 of the Town and Country Planning Act, 1959, that any applicant for planning permission must give notice of the application to the owner of the affected land, and to certain other people including tenants of agricultural holdings. Previously there had been no such provision, and it had been quite possible for a developer to be given permission to use land for, say, opencast ironstone workings without the knowledge of either the owner or tenant farmers affected. Under section 37 the owners and tenants may object to the application giving grounds in writing. They may in practice be invited to make oral representations, but there is no express right to do so. If the application is granted the objectors have no further rights. If, however, the application is refused and the applicant appeals to the Minister, the objectors will have their opportunity to intervene if a local Public Inquiry is held.

The other important improvement relates to the procedure at Inquiries. Where a Public Inquiry is held upon some planning proposal upon which a positive view has been advanced by any Government department, then a representative of that department must be present at the Inquiry and available for cross-examination by the applicants or objectors. In these circumstances the official may not be cross-examined on matters of policy but he may be asked about the factual evidence, e.g., quality of land, upon which his advice was based.

PART V

LOVE THY NEIGHBOUR

It has been said that the biblical injunction to love one's neighbour takes on a restricted and negative form in the hands of the lawyers. It becomes a simple duty not to injure one's neighbour in certain ways.

In this part of the book we shall look at some of the legal duties which a farmer owes to his neighbours in general, and we shall see how far the ordinary law of the land places restraints upon his right to do as he likes with his own land, buildings, machinery and stock. On the brighter side we shall deal with some of the means whereby a farmer may protect himself and his farm from the misdemeanours of neighbours or indeed the public in general.

Chapter 23

TRESPASS AND MALICIOUS DAMAGE

Trespass to land is one of the oldest misdeeds known to English law. In the unsettled times which followed the Norman conquest the King's judges were quick to remedy any interference with the lawful possession and enjoyment of land. Gradually the scope of the remedy was extended, so that today any " direct injury " to land (including a mere crossing of the boundary, since this must " injure " the land, however slightly) may be a trespass.

In the unsettled times which followed the Norman conquest.

But trespass has never been a crime in our law. It is simply a " tort " or civil wrong for which the courts will grant a remedy by way of injunction or damages at the suit of the injured party. A crime differs from a tort in that it constitutes an offence against the public in general (although injuries to particular citizens may result from it) and consequently the State, as representing the public, takes upon itself the prosecution and punishment of crimes. The injured party " sues ", the State " prosecutes ".

The old empty threat TRESPASSERS WILL BE PROSECUTED may still be seen on some estates, and it is not easy to think of a more accurate alternative. Perhaps TRESPASSERS *MAY* BE PROSECUTED is the solution, because there is one case, well-known to gamekeepers, in which a trespasser may be committing a crime as well as a tort. It is an offence under section 30 of the Game Act, 1831, for any person to trespass upon land in the daytime "in search or pursuit of game, or woodcocks, snipes, quails, landrails, or conies (rabbits) ", and he is liable on conviction before the magistrates to a fine of £20 plus costs.

In recent years cases of trespass by youngsters armed with air rifles or even more dangerous weapons have been all too common, and the criminal law is not always adequate to deal with them. These juvenile desperadoes may not be looking for game or even " conies "; they may be quite happy to take pot-shots at anything that moves. Frequently the malicious damage laws cover cases of this kind. There are various offences under the Malicious Damage Act, 1861, the Larceny Act, 1916, and the Criminal Justice Act, 1914, which empower the magistrates to enforce varying penalties according to the extent of the damage together with a power in some cases to order compensation. But there is a serious malicious damage problem in areas of new housing development, and many offenders still go unpunished.

In an action for trespass at common law the plaintiff need not prove that he has actually suffered damage. The law presumes that damage will automatically result from a trespass; but naturally evidence of the actual loss or injury suffered will affect the court's decision as to the amount of damages to be awarded. Thus if the trespasser is caught and prosecuted for malicious damage, a farmer may be compensated there and then by order of the Bench. But failing this he may still be entitled to bring an action in the County Court (or the High Court if the damage is more than £400) and recover the amount of his loss. A common difficulty is the lack of funds so frequently enjoyed by this type of offender. It may be worth noting that a club or a school may be liable for the acts of its members if it has given its implied authority for the acts complained of or if it has been negligent in allowing matters to get out of hand. Whether or not he may intend to bring an action for damages, a farmer (as an occupier) is legally entitled to evict a trespasser, and for this purpose he may use reasonable force if the trespasser refuses to leave. But the perennial question of what is reasonable makes this a difficult remedy in practice.

Trespass by visitors

By no means all acts of trespass arise directly from the crossing of the farm boundary by a stranger. To give but two examples, a trespass may result when a person abuses his right to pass and repass along a highway or when a person exceeds some limited right to use the air-space above land. This is illustrated by the famous case of *Harrison v. Duke of Rutland*, 1893, where the duke succeeded in satisfying the court that he was entitled to use reasonable force to remove Harrison from the highway adjoining his land on the ground that Harrison had abused the highway for the purpose of scaring away grouse from his Lordship's butts! Another example arises where a person, having entered upon land for some lawful purpose or in the exercise of some legal right, then proceeds to do something which renders his presence upon the land unlawful. This is known as trespass *" ab initio "* (i.e., from the beginning). His wrongful act makes him a trespasser and relates back to the moment of entry.

This rule, whereby a person being lawfully upon land may suddenly become a trespasser merely by committing some wrongful act, may have some interesting consequences. Modern cases are few, but on at least one occasion the rule has been invoked to restrain an official who had overstepped his powers, and there is clearly a moral here for those engaged on surveys or default actions, or other unwelcome visitors to farms, who go there " in pursuance of statutory powers ".

Litter

Before we leave the related subjects of trespass and malicious damage by humans, it will be as well to mention the growing problem of litter. Inevitably the townsman at leisure is drawn in increasing numbers to the most beautiful parts of the country within his reach, and regrettably the " Keep Britain Tidy " campaign has not been completely successful in restraining him from leaving unsightly and often dangerous mementos of his visits. The Litter Act, 1960, does give some measure of protection from this particular curse. Unfortunately for the farmer the Act goes scarcely far enough, because it applies only to litter deposited " in, into or from any place in the open air to which the public are entitled or permitted to have access without payment ". This is a punishable offence. But if a party of picnickers, instead of heaving their rubbish over the hedge from the highway, actually come and camp out in the field leaving their broken bottles and other paraphernalia behind them, they cannot then be prosecuted under this Act, though their conduct may, of course, amount to wilful damage.

Chapter 24

CATTLE TRESPASS

Cattle trespass is like human trespass only more so! It involves nothing more than an escape resulting from the breach of some legally recognised duty to fence. The person having control (usually the owner) of cattle is liable for any damage they may do by straying upon neighbouring land. " Cattle " in this sense extends to all types of farm stock, including poultry. It is, of course, the old legal meaning of cattle and has the same derivation as the word chattle—a very wide term covering personal or movable property generally. Cats and dogs, oddly enough, are excluded from the expression " cattle ", and so in general their owners will

Cattle trespass is like human trespass only more so.

not be liable in cattle trespass for their misdeeds. The liability is a heavy one—it is not necessary for a plaintiff to show that the owner of the cattle has been negligent—and an action will succeed simply on proof of damage, following the escape of the cattle from their own land, unless the defendant can establish one or other of the recognised defences.

Defences

The most important defence is that the plaintiff was himself in breach of some legal duty to fence. Such a duty might arise by agreement, custom, prescription or statute. If by agreement, the agreement must be between the same parties. It would be no defence, for example, that the plaintiff owed a duty to his landlord or some other third party to keep the fence in repair. If by customary or prescriptive duty, the custom or prescription must be established by proof of long user. The best example arises in connection with common land. By custom (or sometimes by virtue of an Inclosure Award) the occupiers of enclosed land

175

adjoining a common, must keep the fences stockproof *against* animals lawfully upon the common. In such a case the commoners would not be liable for damage done by their sheep or cattle to adjoining land, unless they had turned out too many animals to graze, in which case they would be exceeding their *lawful* grazing rights. Statutory duties to fence are rare by comparison, but quite frequently a corporation may be under such a duty, and the British Transport Commission inherited some extensive fencing duties from the old railway companies. Duties of this kind may be varied by contract, and the deeds of railway-infested farms frequently contain " release " clauses showing that the owner or his predecessors have accepted a lump sum in lieu of the right to have their own land fenced in perpetuity against the railway.

Remedies

The remedy of damages, with or without an injunction to restrain further acts of trespass, has always been available in actions for cattle trespass. But legal proceedings are not always practicable, particularly if the damage is slight. However, the law recognises a form of self-help very closely similar to the eviction of a trespasser. This is the charming and picturesque remedy of " distress damage feasant ". Another form of distress has already been discussed (page 6) in relation to rent. The essence of this one is that the person seizing the trespassing cattle has normally no right to dispose of them. He may hold them, however, and may exercise a kind of lien over them until the owner claims them and pays for the damage they may have done. The distrainor would also seem to be entitled to a further sum for the cost of feeding and keeping the cattle until they are claimed. The question sometimes arises as to whether a distrainor may eventually acquire a right to dispose of stock if the owner fails to claim them. There appears to be no case law to give any direct assistance, but we think that in practice the distrainor could safely sell the stock after waiting a reasonable time to give the owner an opportunity to claim them. Obviously he should sell at the best price available, because if they were later claimed he would be liable for their value (less damage and cost of keep). In Wales it is not uncommon for local authorities to impound sheep straying from common land and in due course to sell them or charge the owner a fixed sum per beast; but this is a statutory remedy, and indeed most urban authorities have powers to deal with stray livestock under the Town Police Clauses Acts.

Animals and the highway

In general farm animals may be driven along the highway, and the owner will not be liable for any incidental damage they may cause unless he has been negligent. If while being lawfully driven along the highway they escape from it and cause damage, again,

apart from negligence there will be no liability. In *Tillet v. Ward,*
1882, an ox, which was being driven along the highway in a market
town got into an adjoining ironmonger's shop and ran amok. It
was held that in the circumstances, negligence not having been
proved against the drover, the owner was not liable.

Escapes on to the highway

If cattle escape from adjoining land on to the highway and cause
damage, then again, unless he has been negligent in some way,
the owner will not be liable. In *Brock v. Richards,* 1951, where a
mare jumped over a fence and injured a motor-cyclist on the highway, the Court of Appeal, after a detailed review of the authorities
on this branch of the law, held that the owner of the mare would
not be liable. The decision has met with a good deal of criticism,
and in 1953 the Goddard Committee on Liability for Animals
recommended that the rule should be reversed or at least severely
qualified by Parliament. The recommendation was not acceptable
to the Government, but obviously there is a serious conflict of
interests here between farmers and road-users. The farmers' case,
in essence, is that fast traffic is a modern development. Road
safety is by and large a matter of public responsibility. Railways
were required to be fenced at the expense of the Railway Companies. Motorways are in fact fenced by the Ministry of Transport,
although the Minister will not admit to any legal duty in that
behalf! Accordingly they argue it would be both inconsistent and
unfair, bearing in mind the vast stretches of upland roads in this
country which have never been fenced, to place this burden upon
the occupiers of adjoining land.

Strangely enough, although no civil liability arises it may be an
offence against the Highways Act, 1959, to allow any cattle, sheep,
horse, mare, gelding or a variety of other animals, to " stray upon
or lie about any highway ". There is a fine of 5s. per beast, subject
to a maximum of 30s.

Animals being driven

In rounding up and driving home cattle which have escaped on
to the highway, a modicum of care should be used. In *Richmond-
Watson v. Rymes Coaches,* 1959, there were cross-claims for negligence following a collision between a motor-bus and some
Aberdeen-Angus heifers which were being rounded up. In the
event both the claim and counter-claim were dismissed, the
Divisional Court holding that in the circumstances negligence had
not been established on either side. But although the coach-
owners' claim for negligence failed in this case, the court made
it clear that a claim in negligence would succeed if, for example,
an unreasonable number of cattle were allowed to be in charge
of one drover. What is reasonable in this sense would, of course,

depend on all the surrounding circumstances, including the amount of traffic which might be expected to use the road. In these highly mechanised days there appears to be a growing tendency in some parts of England to drive cattle from the seat of a tractor. As yet the courts have not had to pronounce upon the practice!

It remains to consider the cases where animals, having strayed on to the highway, subsequently wander from the highway itself on to adjoining land and do damage. Long ago it was held (in *Dovaston v. Payne*, 1795) that in this type of case the owner will be liable. It is a common enough happening in areas of unfenced roads, although sheep seem to be fairly harmless creatures and do not normally wreak great havoc and destruction unless, of course, they get far enough from their natural stamping ground to find a luscious well-kept private garden.

The extent of damages

Finally, a word about the type of damage for which an owner will be liable in an action for cattle trespass. In general the liability extends to all types of damage which the owner might reasonably be expected to foresee. This has been held to include the spread of disease (see *Theyer v. Purnell*, 1918). It certainly covers the more obvious kinds of damage to land or crops caused by munching, trampling or rootling.

Chapter 25

DANGEROUS ANIMALS

In the last chapter, particularly in dealing with the common law action for cattle trespass, we were mainly considering injuries to land. The damage which animals may cause to human beings or other animals by such viciousness as biting, kicking or worrying belongs to a different realm in law into which we now pass.

The guiding principle here is that if we keep a dangerous animal the law says we must keep it at our peril and we shall be liable for the damage it may cause. But the common law has developed the principle over a very wide field, so that the question " Is this a dangerous animal? " may be answered differently according to the surrounding circumstances in each case.

What animals are dangerous ?

The question must be answered in two stages. Some animals are considered dangerous by their very nature. These animals, " *ferae naturae* ", include most of the animals which would be

The camel is a borderline case.

labelled dangerous in a zoo. Animals not indigenous to Great Britain are almost invariably counted as dangerous by nature, provided they have the wherewithal to injure mankind and a

179

reputed inclination to do so. Lions, tigers, and leopards are obvious candidates. The camel is a borderline case and has indeed been held (in *McQuaker v. Goddard,* 1940) to be not dangerous by its nature in England. We will not prolong this discussion of animals *ferae naturae* except to refer to that highly lucrative species of farm livestock, the mink. There are some 500 mink farms in England and Wales, and the havoc escaped mink can wreak amongst poultry is well known to farmers in Hampshire. Whilst there is no case law in point, the mink is not indigenous to this country. It is uniformly vicious, having a great deal in common with stoats and weasels, and we have little doubt that it would be classed as an animal *ferae naturae.* Unfortunately the virtual impossibility of marking a mink—they are highly neurotic creatures —makes it difficult to identify offenders, even assuming they can be caught. Animals of this class are, of course, kept strictly at the owner's peril, and the owner—or, to be strictly accurate, the person having control of them, who may not always be the owner— will be fully liable for all foreseeable damage they may cause.

All other animals, including all ordinary farm animals, fall upon the other side of the " dangerous " line and are known collectively to lawyers as animals "*mansuetae naturae*", i.e., normally well-disposed towards mankind. Dogs also belong here. A person who suffers injury or loss from an animal in this class must in general pass over two hurdles in order to succeed with an action for damages. He must show:

(a) that the defendant knew of the animal's dangerous pro- pensity; and

(b) that the injury or damage arose from the particular dangerous propensity which was known to the defendant.

The action is known as the " scienter " action (from the Latin *scio,* I know) because of the importance of the defendant's know- ledge of the danger, and all claims arising from horse-kicks, dog-bites, sheep-worrying and the like must pass both these tests to succeed. This is the origin of the expression " A dog is allowed one bite ", which is not strictly accurate. The dog may have bitten before and its owner may still be unaware of its inclination to bite mankind. The owner's knowledge is the vital thing.

Marauding dogs

The protection of livestock from dogs is a subject of special interest, particularly so in the " sub-rural " areas where townsmen bring their dogs or simply leave them to wander at will. In some countries (e.g., Australia) there is very strict control of all dogs by means of registration; and it has often been argued that more stringent measures should be taken in this country, particularly to deal with the growing army of stray dogs which the Dog-Lovers'

League has estimated at half-a-million in 1960. It seems that many people turn their dogs loose at six months old instead of buying a licence, and a proportion of these inevitably revert to the vocation originally assigned to them by providence of keeping down the sheep and poultry population.

To some extent the Dogs Act, 1906, and the Dogs (Protection of Livestock) Act, 1953, are helpful. They make it a punishable offence, both for the owner and for the person in charge of a dog, if the dog "worries livestock on agricultural land". Worrying livestock is defined in section 1 (2) of the 1953 Act as:

(a) attacking livestock; or
(b) chasing livestock in such a way as may reasonably be expected to cause injury or suffering to the livestock or, in the case of females, abortion or loss of or diminution in their produce.

The Act contains a very exhaustive definition of "livestock" as meaning "cattle, sheep, goats, swine, horses or poultry", and for this purpose poultry means "domestic fowls, turkeys, geese or ducks".

The Act of 1906 begins by providing that "the owner of any dog shall be liable in damages for injury done to any cattle by that dog", and no qualifications are expressed. However, the Act of 1953 makes it a statutory defence, at least for the purposes of a prosecution under that Act, for the defendant to show that the livestock are trespassing. It would also appear to be a defence to a civil claim that the plaintiff or his servant had provoked the dog, or that the plaintiff or his servant had been in some way guilty of contributory negligence.

A last resort

"When may I shoot a dog that gets amongst my stock?" is a perennial question. In shooting a dog in these circumstances a farmer is really exercising a remedy of self-help (similar to distress damage feasant, discussed at page 176) for the defence of his property. If he pulls the trigger too soon he may be liable in damages to the owner of the dog; if he leaves matters too late he may lose a season's lambs. The rule is clearly expressed in a decision of the Court of Appeal in *Cresswell v. Sirl,* 1948. In order to justify the shooting the farmer must be able to show:

(a) that the dog was actually attacking the livestock, or that he had attacked them and was about to renew the attack; *and*
(b) that the shooting was the only reasonable means of preventing the damage or further damage.

In other words dogs, like burglars, must not be regarded as fair game to be shot on sight. There must have been an " attack ", and there must be no other reasonable means available to ward off injury.

A comparatively recent illustration of the principle laid down in *Cresswell v. Sirl* is provided by the case of *Thayer v. Newman*, 1953. Here the facts were unusual in that the shooting was done not by the farmer but by a police constable acting on the farmer's behalf, and in this sense as his agent. This did not, however, materially affect the decision. A farmer in Monmouthshire had complained to a police constable (P.C. Newman, who lived in a bungalow adjoining the farm) that he had been losing sheep owing to worrying by dogs. Shortly afterwards P.C. Newman saw two dogs chasing a sheep on the farm. He said that he called them to come away, and that one of them obeyed but the other continued to chase the sheep. He thereupon shot the second dog. The owner sued for damages, and the County Court Judge at Tredegar found that the shooting was unjustified on the ground that the dog was playful, not ferocious, and was not chasing the sheep with the intention of killing it. He thought the dog was too small to be able to do much harm, and accordingly ordered P.C. Newman to pay £21 damages. This decision, however, was later reversed in the Court of Appeal, where it was held that even a playful attack could justify shooting, provided that, in all the circumstances, shooting was the only reasonable means of protecting the livestock from imminent harm.

Chapter 26

NUISANCE AND THE FARMER

The expression "nuisance" has a special and rather narrow significance for lawyers. Usually it takes the form either of an indirect injury to land (remembering that land includes buildings) or an interference with the enjoyment of land. The spirit of "live and let live" has not been absent in the development of the law of nuisance, and by no means every interference will give rise to an action. Buildings that spoil the view are the best example of this. In one sense they are a very real interference with the enjoyment of property, but the courts have consistently held that these do not constitute a nuisance—though it may be otherwise if they are so close as to interfere with rights of light. To found an action for nuisance at common law there must have been "a substantial interference with a reasonable standard of comfort". The general character of the neighbourhood has often been of crucial importance in considering what is reasonable in this sense, and it has been said that events which might be accepted with equanimity in Bermondsey may well amount to a nuisance in Belgrave Square. In the case of a continuing nuisance the court may grant an injunction; but in general the remedy of damages is available to compensate the plaintiff for his injury or loss.

Public nuisances

What we have said above applies to the common law civil action for nuisance. This kind of nuisance is a tort, and is sometimes referred to as private nuisance. Some nuisances, however, are prohibited by statute, and these are referred to collectively as public nuisances. There is a summary procedure under the Public Health Act, 1936, under which local authorities may deal simply with public nuisances by means of abatement notices backed up by default powers (i.e., the local authority may do the work involved in abating a nuisance themselves and recover the reasonable cost from the offender). It is also an offence to ignore such a notice, for which the Magistrates' Courts have power to impose a fine or imprisonment. Most of the public nuisances expressly prohibited under the Act of 1936 are those considered to be prejudicial to public health, like the blocking of drains or sewers. Later legislation has added substantially to the list of public nuisances, all of which may be dealt with under the same summary procedure. Highway nuisances are many and varied: a smoke nuisance was created by section 16 of the Clean Air Act, 1956, and the Noise Abatement Act, 1960, has made it a public nuisance to make an excessive noise if at least three householders are aggrieved.

A public nuisance to make an excessive noise.

The farmer as a defendant in nuisance

What farming activities are most likely to result in proceedings for nuisance? The answer largely depends on the neighbours and indeed the neighbourhood. There have been several cases in the courts involving nuisance arising from the keeping of farm animals; and, strangely, this is not entirely a modern phenomenon. Indeed Professor Glanville Williams in his " Liability for Animals " says " the stench of pigs kept in towns was too much even for hardened medieval nostrils and became a regular subject of indictment in the leet. The same remedy was applied to the pollution of a neighbour's well from a stable. These principles were adopted by the common law courts which held that keeping swine in a city was a nuisance at common law and that an action on the case lay for erecting a hog-sty so near the house of the plaintiff that the air thereof was corrupted ".

It should be noted, however, that the cause of action has no necessary connection with the animals themselves. The nuisance may arise from the noise, filth or stench according to the circumstances, and it is this which is objectionable and gives rise to proceedings, not the mere presence of the animals. A good modern illustration of the application of the principles of nuisance to the keeping of animals is provided by the case of *Leeman v. Montagu,* 1936. In that case an injunction was granted to restrain a farmer from keeping cockerels in undue numbers in his orchard at Thorpe in the East Riding of Yorkshire, a district which was described as "partly rural but largely residential". About 750 cockerels were being kept in the orchard which was about 100 yards from the neighbour's house.

The keeping of livestock is by no means the only facet of a farmer's activities which may bring him into contact with the law of nuisance. For example, it has been held that an occupier of land who burns weeds so near to the boundary of his own land that damage ensues to the property of his neighbour, may be liable (*Tuberville v. Stamps,* 1697). Overhanging trees are a frequent source of complaint, and if trees overhang a neighbour's boundary in such a way as to interfere with the neighbour's enjoyment of his land (e.g., in the case of yew trees by poisoning his cattle) the owner of the trees would be liable. The spraying of liquid manure and the use of chemical sprays applied from the air, both controversial in themselves, involve serious hazards from the point of view of nuisance. Aerial spraying fortunately is normally undertaken by contractors, most of whom have agreed to accept the general conditions of the Aerial Spray Code. It is advisable to ensure, however, that the spraying contract does not pass on this heavy liability to the farmer.

It is sometimes suggested that to harbour weeds, at least in excessive quantities, if this resulted in damage to neighbouring land, might be an actionable nuisance. It was held, however (in *Giles v. Walker,* 1890) where a farmer had failed consistently to keep down his thistles, that no action lay in these circumstances. Although a statutory duty now exists to clear land of weeds (page 82) the duty so imposed does not seem to arise until the occupier has been served with a notice to cut down and destroy them.

Defences

It may sometimes be an effective defence to an action for nuisance if the defendant can show that he has been pursuing the course of conduct complained of for a substantial period. This is because the " long user " of land in a way which would otherwise involve a nuisance will, provided the use has been exercised openly and as of right, give rise to a prescriptive right to do the act complained of. In at least one 19th century case (*Baxendale v. McMurray,* 1867) it was held that a right to pollute a stream may be acquired in this way.

The difficulty about prescriptive rights as a defence to an action for nuisance is that one cannot acquire a prescriptive right to commit a criminal offence. Thus, for example, pollution of rivers or streams now constitutes an offence generally under section 2 of the Rivers (Prevention of Pollution) Act, 1951, and in these circumstances we seriously doubt whether a defence based on prescription would be successful nowadays in a civil action for nuisance based on pollution.

The farmer as plaintiff in nuisance

By any standards agriculture, as an industry, must be accepted as being peculiarly vulnerable to outside interference. Both arable and livestock farming involve special risks in a largely industrialised country, and there is no shortage of decided cases to illustrate the difficulties. Unfortunately, a farmer plaintiff does not necessarily win an action based on nuisance merely by showing that a neighbour is pursuing a course of conduct which interferes with his farming operations. The position has been expressed in the House of Lords as follows:

"A balance has to be maintained between the right of the occupier to do what he likes with his own and the right of his neighbour not to be interfered with. It is impossible to give any precise or universal formula but it may broadly be said that a useful test is perhaps what is reasonable according to the ordinary usages of mankind living in society".

In many of the cases locality has been the overriding factor. The courts have recognised that there is a national policy of segregating different uses of land, and have furthered this policy by taking into account whether the defendant is putting his land to a use which is compatible with the main use to which land in that district is put. Thus, other things being equal, there would be a better chance of succeeding with a claim for nuisance based on, say, air pollution by cement dust from a factory, if the factory happened to be situated in the heart of pleasant countryside. Not all the cases involve a clash of urban and rural interests. For example, in *Farrer v. Nelson*, 1885, a lessee of sporting rights who was so successful in breeding game that a neighbour's crops were damaged was held to be liable in nuisance (see page 26).

A "substantial interference" there must be, and this interference must undoubtedly assume some physical form. For this reason noise is never an easy ground for an action in nuisance. In *Hollywood Silver Fox Farm Ltd. v. Emmett*, 1936, the court held that the firing of guns out of spite against the plaintiff with the object of interfering with the breeding of silver foxes by him was actionable, but it emphasised that its finding of malice was an important factor in the decision. Once the substantial interference has been proved, however, (whether by dust, smoke, fumes, noise, filth, or otherwise) it will be no defence for the defendant merely to plead that the plaintiff's mode of livelihood required unusually favourable conditions. Thus the Privy Council (in *McKinnon Industries Ltd. v. Walker*, 1951, decided that once the interference is proved the remedies for that interference will extend to such a sensitive and delicate operation as the growing of orchids; the damage to the orchids was a foreseeable consequence of what had already been proved to be a nuisance, and at that stage the orchids' hypersensitiveness became irrelevant.

Finally a serious difficulty arises in areas where farming is inter-spersed with industry as in Bedfordshire (brickmaking), the West Riding of Yorkshire (steelmaking) and Staffordshire (ceramics). Here the pollution, particularly air pollution, may be caused by a number of defendants. In a famous case (*Pride of Derby and Derbyshire Angling Association v. British Celanese Ltd.,* 1953) where the owners of fishing rights brought a successful action for nuisance against the defendants, whose effluent had been polluting the Trent, it was held that each was liable to the extent that his interference had caused damage. Obviously the apportionment of liability is not an easy matter, and might prove a serious embarrass-ment where, for example, several brick companies were emitting fluorine fumes in the same area; but we think the court would follow the *Pride of Derby* decision and make a reasonable appor-tionment.

Chapter 27

NEGLIGENCE AND
DANGEROUS PREMISES

Most farming operations do not involve great risks from the point of view of negligence, but farmers, like others, are bound by the ordinary everyday rules which affect them in their dealings with their fellow men either as motorists on the highway or as occupiers of their farms. We therefore deal with the subjects of negligence and dangerous premises together.

During the past 50 years negligence has become perhaps the most important of the torts or civil wrongs, and its scope as a cause of action is very wide indeed. The leading case, well known to lawyers and to many laymen as the snail in the bottle case, was

Most farming operations do not involve great risks.

a decision of the House of Lords in *Donoghue v. Stevenson*, 1932. In that case the House of Lords laid down the general principles to be applied where the plaintiff relies on the breach of a duty of care by the defendant which has resulted in damage to him. The facts in the case were that two women entered a shop, and one of them ordered some ginger beer to be consumed by the other. A stone bottle was produced containing ginger beer, of which the greater part was poured into a glass and consumed by the younger of the two women. When the remainder was poured out it was seen that the bottle had been harbouring the decomposed remains of a snail. The young lady suffered severe shock, became seriously ill, and brought an action for negligence against the manufacturers. This not over-inspiring material brought from Lord Atkin the judgment which has become famous in legal history. " The rule ", he said, " that you are to love your neighbour becomes in law, you must not injure your neighbour; and the lawyers question: ' Who is my neighbour? ' receives a restricted reply. You must take reasonable care to avoid acts or omissions which you can reasonably foresee would be likely to injure your neighbour. Who, then, in law, is my neighbour? The answer seems to be, persons who are so closely and directly affected by my act that I ought reasonably to have them in contemplation as being so affected, when I am directing my mind to the acts or omissions which are called in question."

To summarise this, as it has been frequently summarised in judgments following the *Donoghue* case, for the plaintiff to succeed in an action for negligence he must show:

(a) that the defendant owed him a duty of care;

(b) that the defendant had been in breach of that duty; and

(c) that he (the plaintiff) had suffered damage in result.

The situations and relationships in which a common law duty of care in this sense can arise are infinite, and we will not overburden this chapter with examples. The duty of a motorist to take care not to injure other road users has already been briefly mentioned. The duty of care owed by an employer (quite apart from his statutory obligations under the Factories Acts or farm safety legislation) has been dealt with at page 98. A third and very important example of this type of legal duty is the duty of a manufacturer to exercise care towards those into whose hands his product may come. If, for example, a manufacturer of agricultural machinery were to place on the market a machine which proved to be dangerous, he might well be liable in negligence to persons injured as a result. The duty in this case would probably not apply to every defect of the machine. We do not think it would apply to a defect which ought to have been apparent upon a reasonable examination. It is clear, however, from such cases as *Grant v. Australian Knitting Mills Limited,* 1936, that if goods are defective and consequently dangerous, then provided the plaintiff can show that the danger must have been present when the goods left the manufacturer it will not be necessary for him to " lay his finger on the exact person in all the chain who was responsible or to specify what he did wrong ". Clearly in these days of complex manufacturing processes it would be invidious to require a plaintiff to go further than to prove that the machine as supplied was dangerous because of some inherent defect.

Damage must not be too remote

We have been discussing the ingredients of negligence as a tort, but the plaintiff would not necessarily succeed merely by establishing that the breach of a legal duty of care had resulted in injury to him. He would also have to show that the damage was such as the law recognises as being reasonably likely to flow from a breach of the particular duty of care. In other words, he must show that damage was not too " remote " from the defendant's act. The defendant will be liable for any loss or damage which could reasonably have been foreseen.

Thus, if A negligently runs into and kills B's heifer, A would be liable first for the loss of the heifer itself, because this is clearly foreseeable. If the heifer were in calf he would be liable for the loss of the calf and lactation, because it is reasonably foreseeable that any given heifer may be in calf. If, however, by some extraordinary chance B had found a buyer for the heifer who was willing to pay something like double her market value, A would not be liable for the loss of profit on this abortive deal, because though goods do frequently change hands at well above their market value, it is not reasonably foreseeable that they will do so.

Contributory negligence

In an action for negligence it is the plaintiff's task to prove that the injury he suffered was caused by the defendant. Sometimes the defendant will argue that, although he may have been negligent, the plaintiff failed to take reasonable care for his own safety and the damage would not have been done but for that reason.

This constitutes " contributory negligence ", and may make it difficult to decide where indeed the real responsibility lay. The principle adopted in such cases is laid down in the Law Reform (Contributory Negligence) Act, 1945, whereby damages are apportioned in relation to the blame. The act does not allow contributory negligence as a complete defence allowing the defendant to escape scot free. It merely says that where a person suffers injury partly through his own fault, the damages awarded shall be reduced according to his share of responsibility for the harm done.

Dangerous premises

The liability of occupiers for injuries occurring to users of their premises is closely akin to negligence, although it is commonly regarded as a separate tort.

The Occupiers Liability Act, 1957, classifies persons entering upon premises (which incidentally includes ships, trains, caravans, scaffolding, etc.) into two classes: lawful visitors and trespassers. Towards visitors the occupier owes a " common duty of care ".

This is defined as a duty " to take such care as in all the circumstances of the case is reasonable to see that the visitor will be reasonably safe in using the premises for the purposes for which he is invited or permitted by the occupier to be there." Under the Act, warning notices are not to be treated as absolving the occupier from liability, unless in all the circumstances the notice was sufficient to enable the visitor to be reasonably safe. In practical terms a farmer would owe precisely the same standard of care to his workers employed on the farm, to contractors carrying out a specific job on his behalf, to visiting veterinary surgeons or artificial inseminators, to the driver calling to collect the milk, to Ministry officials, and so forth.

The Act goes on to provide that in the case of tenanted or leasehold properties the primary liability for keeping the premises safe is upon the tenant or lessee. If, however, the danger arises from the failure of the landlord to execute repairs which are his liability under the agreement, the tenant is entitled to be indemnified by the landlord, provided he has given notice of the defect in reasonable time. Thus if the buildings of Headlong Hall Farm are in a state of structural disrepair, with the result that the roof of the implement shed falls in and injures Figaro, the local man-of-all-work, it is more than likely that the tenant, as occupier, will be entitled to indemnification by his landlord against his liability to Figaro. In the absence of written agreement as to the liabilities for repair, one would have to apply the provisions of the repairs regulations discussed in Chapter 2. If, however, precisely the same accident had resulted from a loose tile on the roof of the shed, it is unlikely that the tenant would be entitled to any indemnity.

So much for the occupier's liability towards lawful visitors. At common law even trespassers are entitled to a modicum of consideration from occupiers, and in one case (*Glasgow Corporation v. Taylor,* 1922) it was held that the Corporation were under an obligation not to plant dangerous shrubs (i.e., deadly nightshade) in a public park, because they might reasonably be expected to know that small boys would be tempted to invade the enclosure. There have been numerous cases where the courts have held occupiers liable for injuries to children who were technically trespassers on the premises, but we do not know of one affecting children injured whilst wandering at will over farm land.

In sum, because trespassers enter property with no right to do so the occupier's duty is much more limited than it is towards visitors. He must not set hidden traps to catch trespassers, nor do such things as quarry-blasting or felling trees, assuming he knows the trespassers to be there. Otherwise a trespasser must take premises as he finds them. If he kneels on a hayfork while seeking a place to doss down in the barn, he has no grounds for bringing an action.

Chapter 28

RIVERS AND STREAMS

The free use of natural water supplies has always been taken for granted in agriculture, but with the growth of urban populations there has been in recent years mounting concern amongst water authorities, whose prime obligation is to satisfy the domestic and industrial needs of urban consumers, to conserve existing resources. In 1958 the Ministry of Housing and Local Government reported that upon one farm which they had surveyed the consumption of water over a period of 12 months was equivalent to the amount which would be required to supply domestic users in a small town.

Against this background the question "How much water can I use, and for what purposes?" takes on an almost political flavour. We shall do our best to give the lawyers' answer, based on such common law rights as exist, but with regard to the various inroads which have been made upon these rights by statute in recent years.

The "riparian" owner of land adjacent to a river or stream is entitled at common law to certain fixed rights. He owns the soil and minerals lying under the bed of the stream as far as mid-stream. He is entitled to exercise fishing rights, and he is entitled to free use of the water provided that this use does not interfere with the similar rights of riparian owners downstream. It is settled law that he may take enough water for his domestic needs and for the purpose of watering his livestock. It is not clear, however, whether he may go further and take supplies for irrigation. The rule as to rights of abstraction was laid down in *Young v. Bankier Distillery,* 1893. Riparian owners are entitled to abstract supplies from the running water in rivers and streams provided that this does not interfere with the right of riparian owners lower down to receive water in its natural state substantially undiminished in quantity and unimpaired in quality. The fact that irrigation involves considerable loss of water by evaporation, only a small percentage of the water succeeding in percolating back to the source, makes it unlikely in practice that riparian rights of abstraction extend to cover the use of water for this purpose.

The position is the same for underground streams where water is flowing in a defined channel. Where, however, water is merely percolating through the soil it is open to the landowner to abstract such percolating water by sinking boreholes or pumping; and it is apparently open to him to take unlimited quantities in this way.

It was held, in *Bradford Corporation v. Pickles,* 1895, that this is so even though the abstraction may result in the drying up of wells on neighbouring land, and the owner of the wells will have no remedy in these circumstances. Rights to abstract percolating water must now be exercised subject to section 14 of the Water Act, 1945, under which the Minister of Housing and Local Government has power to make orders for the conservation of underground water supplies in certain areas. Orders under section 14

Power to make orders for the conservation of underground water supplies.

have been made in most areas of water scarcity. The effect of these orders in areas where section 14 applies is that no new wells or boreholes may be constructed without the Minister's licence.

In some cases special rights for the use of water may have been acquired by custom or prescription. Thus a riparian owner may acquire a right to pen back a stream or to direct a part of a stream by means of an obstruction placed in its natural course, provided that such activities would not interfere with navigation in a navigable river. It may be that the right to use water for irrigation could be acquired in this way, and indeed it has been held (in *Sampson v. Hoddinott,* 1856) that interference by a higher riparian owner with the natural flow of the water course, upsetting the custom of the tenants of a lower riparian owner to irrigate their water meadows, was actionable.

PART VI

HUNTING, SHOOTING AND FISHING

Most of what we have to say in this part emerges from the game laws, a subject so complex that writers invariably begin by declaring how impossible they are. In confirming the truth of this, we add the customary limitation, that all we can do is to outline the parts most likely to concern the reader for whom we are writing—in this case the farmer. The questions he is most likely to raise are: what birds and beasts may I slay on my farm; when may I kill them; what licences do I need; what rights and wrongs in them have other folk?

Chapter 29

GAME AND WILD BIRDS

We need first to sort out what creatures we mean when we speak of "game". There is no overall definition. Different Acts of Parliament give different definitions for their particular purposes.

What creatures we mean when we speak of "game".

In the Acts whose provisions we deal with, the following are included:

Game Act, 1831—hares, pheasants, partridges, grouse, heath or moor game, black game.

Night Poaching Act, 1828—as above, with bustards added.

Poaching Prevention Act, 1862—as for the Game Act, but with the addition of woodcock, snipe, rabbits and the eggs of pheasants, partridges, grouse and black or moor game.

Game Licences Act, 1860—as for the Game Act, plus woodcock, snipe, deer and rabbits.

Agricultural Holdings Act, 1948—deer, pheasants, partridges, grouse and black game. This definition has to do with a tenant's right to claim compensation for damage by game, which we have discussed at page 24.

Finally, the Ground Game Act, 1880, defines ground game as meaning hares and rabbits.

Who owns the game?

Because game birds and animals are by nature wild, the general rule is that no man can claim them absolutely as his property.

197

This means that, among other things, a poacher who makes off with a pocketful of hares is not a thief in the eyes of the law; although as a trespasser he may find himself in well-deserved trouble. But when game is reclaimed, as it is sometimes called, for instance where young pheasants are being fostered by a broody hen, the poacher who pinches them may end up being prosecuted for larceny.

Once game has been killed or captured it ceases to be nobody's baby and turns into property. This time the general rule is that it belongs to the owner of the land on which it is killed, no matter whether it is killed by himself or, rightly or wrongly, by somebody else. However, unless or until it is dead or gathered it is not his property. For instance, even though a pheasant is fired at and falls beyond hope of survival, a person who fraudulently makes off with it before it is dead or picked up on the landowner's behalf cannot be charged with larceny.

It may simplify these rules to take an imaginary case where two neighbouring farmers are given to sporting on their respective farms, Farmer Green on Greenacre, Farmer Black on Blackacre.

One afternoon Green and his dog go partridge shooting. He kills a brace on his own farm. Clearly enough they become his absolute property.

The third he shoots on his own land; momentum carries it over the boundary and it falls dead on Blackacre. Nevertheless it is still Green's property. He nips over the boundary fence and gathers it up. In so doing he becomes a trespasser.

Back on his own land he wings his fourth partridge. This also descends on Blackacre, but it is sufficiently alive to up and start running. Green pursues it on Black's land and captures it. This time, the bird still living, Green is a poacher as well as a trespasser, although the bird is legally his property. If, however, Green had stayed on his own land and despatched his dog to retrieve the stricken bird, Green would have committed trespass but he would not be poaching.

Hardly has Belle laid the bird at her master's feet on Greenacre, before Green perceives a fifth and sixth partridge approaching him from Black's land. While they are still over Blackacre, Green gives them a right and left. One plummets on Blackacre, the other lands this side of the boundary. In shooting the birds while they flew over his neighbour's farm, Green has committed trespass. The bird that fell on Greenacre is Green's property, however, whereas the one that fell dead on Blackacre is Black's. If, therefore, Green crosses the boundary and gathers it, he is poaching as well as trespassing.

The bemused reader need not be advised that it pays to be on give-and-take terms with his neighbour where sporting is concerned . . .

Young game which cannot stray from home, for instance hand-reared pheasant chicks, are for the time being the absolute property of the owner of their home ground. But once the birds leave home, the owner's absolute property in them becomes qualified.

The property in the eggs of game birds is similar to the property in game, although one might suppose that it followed the rules pertaining to stay-at-home youngsters. But if an owner buys the eggs, or collects them for artificial rearing, they become his property absolutely.

Who may kill game

The common law rule is that the right to kill or take wild creatures belongs to the occupier of the land. Unless there is agreement to the contrary, therefore, a farm tenant, not his land-lord or anyone else, has the exclusive rights. Quite commonly, of course, a landlord will reserve the sporting rights when letting a farm, together with a right of entry to exercise them, and very likely specify the birds he has a mind to slaughter.

Having reserved the sporting rights, the landlord may either enjoy them himself, or let them to sporting tenants. In either event, the tenant-farmer must then restrain his sporting instincts and confine them to killing and taking hares, rabbits and such creatures as are neither reserved to the landlord nor protected under the Protection of Birds Act, 1954. If, in despite, he does kill or take any game on his farm, or allow anyone else to do so, he may be prosecuted and fined.

Where the sporting rights are not reserved, a tenant-farmer can exercise them himself just as though he were the owner. The odd thing here, though, is that (unless the right to kill and take rabbits has been expressly conferred on him) he cannot kill ground game at night with firearms. Alternatively he may let the shooting rights to someone else.

Ground game

Hares and rabbits are the subjects of the Ground Game Acts, 1880 and 1906, which give the occupier of land a right to kill and take them thereon. This is an inalienable right; that is to say, even if he wished to, a tenant-farmer could not rid himself of it.

Consequently, however rigorously a landlord reserves the rights in a tenancy agreement, including among the beasts reserved the hares and rabbits on the farm, the right to kill and take them is at best shared between owner and occupier.

The limitations on the tenant-farmer's exercise of his ground game rights are noted at page 24.

WILD BIRDS

One of the consolations of being a harmless British bird is that the law looks with charity on one's preservation. Most of these humane measures are to be found in the Protection of Birds Act, 1954, which consolidated a number of far older statutes going back to Victorian times.

The schedules to that Act, which read like the index to a bird-lover's handbook, divide the species according to whether they are wholly or partially protected, or not at all. Before sorting them out, it may be noted that " wild bird " does not include those game birds to which the Game Act, 1831, applies, namely pheasant, partridge, grouse or black game.

Schedule 1 is a collection of wild birds and their eggs protected by special penalties.

Those in Part I are protected *at all times*—

Avocet, bee-eater, bittern, snow bunting, bustard, honey buzzard, chough, corn-crake (or landrail), crossbill, divers (black-throated, great northern and red-throated), dotterel, eagle, goshawk, grebe (black-necked and Slavonian), greenshank, hen-harrier, hobby, hoopoe, kite, marsh-harrier, merlin, Montagu's harrier, golden oriole, osprey, peregrine, red-necked phalarope, plover (Kentish and little ringed), quail, black redstart, roller, ruff and reeve, spoonbill, black-winged stilt, Temminck's stint, stone curlew, swan (whooper and Bewick's), tern (black and roseate), tit (bearded and crested), warbler (Dartford and marsh), St. Kilda wren, wryneck.

The effect of this all-time protection is to make it an offence wilfully to kill, injure, or take, or attempt to kill, injure or take either them or their eggs, or to destroy their nests while still in use. Transgressors may be stopped and searched by a constable without warrant, and special penalties—a fine not exceeding £25, or imprisonment up to one month for a first offence—apply to the specially-rated species listed above, and to those in Part II.

Part II birds, however, are specially protected only *during the close season.* They comprise:

Brambling, black-tailed godwit, whimbrel, certain wild duck (common scoter, Garganey teal, goldeneye, long-tailed, scaup, velvet scoter) and the greylag goose.

Schedule 2 gives a catalogue of wild birds which may be killed or taken *at any time* by authorised persons. " Authorised person " means primarily the owner or occupier of land, or anyone given permission by them.

Cormorant, crow (carrion or hooded), domestic pigeons gone wild, gull (greater and lesser black-backed, herring), jackdaw, jay, magpie, rook, shag, house sparrow, sparrow-hawk, starling, stock-dove, wood-pigeon. In some areas the bullfinch and the oyster-catcher are added.

Schedule 3 lists those birds which may be killed or taken *outside the close season.* The distinction between them and the Schedule 1

Part II birds listed earlier is that the penalties for illegally killing or taking them are less severe, namely, a fine not exceeding £5. Furthermore, Schedule 1 protects their eggs as well as the birds themselves.

Capercaillie, coot, curlew (other than stone curlew), bar-tailed godwit, moorhen, plover (golden and grey), redshank, snipe (common and jack), certain wild duck (common pochard, gadwall, mallard, pintail, shoveller, teal, tufted duck, wigeon), certain wild geese (bean-goose, Canada, pink-footed, white-fronted) and woodcock.

It will be seen that a great many well-known birds—cuckoo, robin, skylark, owl, for instance—as well as many less familiar, are not mentioned in the above lists. Their omission is no oversight; it signifies that under the 1954 Act no one may shoot or kill them at any time.

The shooting seasons

For part of the sportman's year it is forbidden to kill or take game or wild birds. The so-called "close season" varies with different species as follows:

Black game—11th December to 19th August.

Capercaillie—1st February to 30th September.

Grouse—11th December to 11th August.

Partridge—2nd February to 31st August.

Pheasant—2nd February to 30th September.

Ptarmigan—11th December to 11th August.

Snipe—1st February to 11th August.

Woodcock—1st February to 30th September.

Wild duck and wild geese, except Barnacle and Brent geese, are protected inland from 1st February to 31st August inclusive; on the foreshore—i.e., below the high water mark of ordinary spring tides—from 21st February to 31st August.

For wild birds generally, where protected by the 1954 Act, the close season lasts from 1st February to 31st August.

A farmer who sports during these close seasons is liable for a fine of up to £1 a head for every game bird killed or taken, plus the costs of his conviction.

Deer enjoy no close season; nor do hares and rabbits, although certain restrictions apply to the latter. Thus the occupier of moorlands and unenclosed non-arable land, although basically he has the rights of any other occupier under the Ground Game Acts, may not kill or take hares or rabbits on such land by any means between 1st April and 31st August inclusive, nor may he shoot them between 1st September and 10th December.

The creatures included in the Game Act, 1831, may not be killed or taken on Sundays and Christmas day; it is an offence to use a dog, gun, net or other implement for the purpose. Moreover, a tenant-farmer may not use a gun to kill hares and rabbits under the Ground Game Acts between the expiration of the first hour after sunset and the beginning of the last hour before sunrise.

Licences to shoot

Users of sporting weapons are liable to provide themselves with one or more of the following: firearm certificates, gun licences, game licences.

Firearm certificates. A firearm in this connection means a sporting rifle or a pistol, as distinct from a shotgun or airgun. Such a certificate is required by any person (with a few exceptions, such as soldiers or policemen) who purchases, possesses, uses or carries any firearm or ammunition for a firearm. It is obtainable from the Chief of Police for the district in which the applicant resides, and costs 5s. for an initial period of three years and 2s. 6d. for renewal. A firearm certificate must be produced when purchasing either firearms or ammunition.

Gun licences apply to smooth-bore shotguns, and are required by any person carrying or using them. A gun licence is also needed for an airgun, air rifle or air pistol, but only if they are carried or used outside the owner's private premises.

A farmer who uses a shotgun to kill vermin (which term, however, does not include rabbits) or for bird-scaring does not need a licence for the purpose. Provided he himself has a gun or game licence, he may authorise some other person to kill his vermin or scare the birds without a licence. A person who holds a game licence does not need a gun licence as well; the greater includes the less.

A gun licence costs 10s. and expires on the following 31st July, no matter on what date it was taken out.

Game licences. Under the Game Licences Act, 1860, a licence is required to kill pheasant, partridge, grouse, black game, moor game, hares, rabbits, woodcock, snipe and deer, not only by shooting but by such other means as snaring or trapping. No licence is needed, however, in the following cases:

(1) To kill rabbits in a warren or enclosed ground, with the permission of the landowner or tenant-farmer.

(2) To kill hares by coursing or hunting.

(3) To kill deer by hunting, or to kill them by other means in enclosed ground with the landlord's consent.

(4) To kill hares and rabbits through the tenant's rights under the Ground Game Acts.

(5) For loaders and beaters, so long as the shots they are serving have the requisite licences.

Game licences are bought from the post office; they all expire on 31st July. The cost depends on the period for which they are taken out, thus:

Licences taken out before 1st November—£3.

Licences taken out on or after 1st November—£2.

Licences taken out for any 14 consecutive days—£1.

A gamekeeper's licence, which allows him to kill game only on his employer's land, costs £2, and also runs to 31st July.

Chapter 30

A MIXED BAG

FISHING

The laws concerning fisheries and rights to fish, like the game laws, can be simplified only by omitting a bumper crop of exceptions and reservations. Here again we limit ourselves, to an outline of the rules of general interest to the waterbound farmer.

The first point is who may fish. This depends, first of all, if the river in question is tidal or not. At common law the public has a general right to fish in the tidal reaches of all rivers, to say nothing of estuaries and the sea itself, but some tidal waters are subject to private or otherwise limited rights.

Non-tidal rivers and streams are another matter. The public has no right to fish in them, even where they are to some extent navigable. The general rule is that the right to fish in non-tidal waters belongs to the landowners on either side. The extent of this right is tied up with the old legal presumptions regarding boundaries. In the absence of any evidence to the contrary, where a river separates two properties, the opposite owners own the soil of the river up to the middle line. The owner of the soil, by

Each owner may legally fish as far as the middle.

another legal presumption, owns the fishery above it. It follows, therefore, that each owner may legally fish as far as the middle and no farther. Quite often, however, one owner will have acquired the exclusive rights, so depriving his opposite number of any rights to fish whatsoever.

Where a farm is let, and nothing to the contrary is agreed in writing, the right to take fish belongs to the tenant. This is a common law right, similar to the right to shoot game. But as with game, the landlord very likely will reserve the fishing rights on letting the farm, and so bar the tenant from indulging in the " contemplative man's recreation ".

Where the rights are specifically reserved, the landlord may either enjoy the fishing himself or let it to a third party, whether an individual or a syndicate. How far he may go in this direction depends, in the first instance, on the wording of the written agreement. Typically the reservation of fishing rights will be supplemented by a power for the landlord or his fishing tenants to enter the farm for the purpose of exercising those rights. In other words, the privilege of fishing is valueless unless the fisherman is legally in a position to haunt the farmer's river banks for the purpose. There may be reserved, too, a right for the landlord or his sporting tenants to trim and lop bushes and trees which would otherwise limit the scope of their casts.

Licences

In Chapter 21 we spoke of the powers and the duties of river boards, notably in connection with land drainage. They also keep an eye on fish, and all persons who angle in river board areas must first obtain a licence. The cost depends on whether game or coarse fish are involved, and varies from one area to another. The board also have powers to levy assessments on riparian owners, to appoint water bailiffs who keep open eyes for unauthorised fishing, to control predatory fish and to contribute towards restocking the waters. An individual who wishes to restock needs the board's prior consent.

Fishing seasons

As with shooting, the taking of fish is forbidden for parts of the year. The seasons are subject to some variation, according to the decree of the river board concerned. Typically one may fish during the following times of year:

Salmon and sea trout—1st February to 1st November.

Trout—2nd March to 1st October.

Fresh water or coarse fish—16th June to 14th March.

HUNTING

The hunt in full chase across the winter wheat is a spectacle to stir the blood—whether to ecstacy or apoplexy depends on how you look at it. A question that often arises in their wake is: have the hunt a legal right to come upon my land, or not? Very often the answer, quite strictly, is no. In real life few farmers object.

Legally, the shadow of trespass hovers over hunting. Trespass, as we demonstrated in Chapter 23, is primarily a wrong committed against the occupation of land; from which it follows that the entry of the hunt is primarily the concern of the occupier.

Strictly speaking the hunt need the occupier's permission to enter, unless they are prepared to risk an action for trespass. It is possible that when letting a farm the landlord might have reserved the right to give the hunt permission to enter, in which event the tenant cannot legally object to his giving them such consent.

This kind of permission to hunt over a farm is called a licence. It may be expressly given, either in writing or by word of mouth, or it may be implied from the fact that no objection has been made to the hunt's visits. In any case, even if a farmer has given express permission, he can withdraw it at any time, either in advance of the next meet or at the moment the field is about to invade his farm.

To follow hounds over a farm after the occupier has warned the hunt to keep off constitutes trespass. Oddly enough, it may seem, even though hounds are in pursuit of a hare, which is legally " game ", it does not go so far as to constitute poaching.

Now comes the query: whom does the offended farmer actually sue for trespass after viewing the shambles bequeathed by the Boxing day meet?

To give a summary answer, the Master of the Hunt is liable for his own trespass and for that of the hunt servants. The responsibility of the hunt followers depends on whether or not they knew that the farmer had forbidden them to enter. If the Master has warned them that Farmer Deerlove won't have them on the place, he is not responsible if they trespass in spite of his warning. Each member is liable for whatever damage he or she may do.

On the other hand, in a case heard in 1816 (*Hume v. Oldacre*), where action for trespass was taken against the huntsman of the Berkeley Hunt, it was held that damage might be recovered not only for the mischief done by the huntsman himself but also for that done by the folk who accompanied him.

Hounds, of course, cannot be expected to respect property rights, and are liable to enter forbidden territory regardless. Provided the Master or the hunt servants do not follow them but make every attempt to whip them off, the Master is not liable for their trespass. If he or the hunt servants *do* enter the forbidden land themselves in order to whip them off, they *are* trespassing. But if it came to an action for trespass, it is hard to imagine that any court would take other than a lenient view of the matter.

POACHING

A poke was once the common word for a small sack or bag, something you blindly bought pigs in. To poach meant, among other things, to ram or tumble things together, into a hole or poke or pocket. Later its meaning expanded to embrace the act of trespassing on other's land to seek or capture game; an action long established as a crime for which the penalties at one time included cutting off the offender's limbs to discourage repeat performances. Today, when poaching has become in many districts an organised means of living, there are some who feel that the penalties have swung from one extreme to another. At any rate, the sentimental view of the poacher as a lovable old rogue with his rightful place in the pattern of country life is less valid than it was a generation back.

The laws against poaching are based on a number of century-and-more old Acts, amended in part in 1960. Some deal with day-time activities, some with night poaching, some with poaching in general. In addition a number of cases have added to what is often admitted as the unsatisfactory confusion of the poaching laws.

To begin with poaching in day-time—which lasts from one hour before sunrise to one hour after sunset: any person who trespasses by day by entering or being upon land in search or pursuit of hare, pheasant, partridges, grouse, heath or moor game, black game, woodcock, snipe or rabbits is guilty of an offence and may be fined on conviction by the magistrates up to £20 plus costs. If five or more people are caught poaching in a gang, each may be fined up to £50 with costs; while if any one of them carries a gun and the person apprehending them is offered violence, menaces or intimidation, a further penalty of £5 may be clapped on them.

It is of course difficult at times to prove that a trespasser was searching for or pursuing a pheasant or one of the specified creatures. Thus, in *Burrows v. Gillingham*, 1893, the sound of a shot had burst out of a wood, and immediately the defendant did likewise with three dogs and ran across the adjoining meadow. He declared that he had fired at a pigeon, and the magistrates accepted his contention and dismissed the case. On taking the matter to a higher court, however, the evidence was considered admissible as proof of the offence, and the magistrates ordered to think again. But this does show the need for having virtually cast-iron evidence that shooting game, etc., not merely pigeons or sparrows, was the intention of any defendant in a court case.

It is not necessary to wait for evidence of poaching before taking action. Day-time poachers may be ordered off the land and asked for their names and addresses, either by the person entitled to the sporting rights, or the farm tenant, or their keepers or servants, or a policeman. If they refuse to quit, or to give their true names and addresses, the person dealing with them may apprehend any such offender and, in the words of section 31 of the Game Act, 1831, " convey him or cause him to be conveyed as soon as conveniently may be before a justice of the peace ". The additional penalty for refusal to leave or give their proper names is a fine up to £5. The apprehending party may seize and forfeit any game in the poacher's possession.

Night poaching

This activity is subject to rather different laws. The Night Poaching Acts, 1828–1844, recognise two separate offences. One is unlawfully taking or destroying any game or rabbits—" game " including the fauna to which the day poaching laws apply—by night, on any open or enclosed land, including the highway and any land, entrances or gates giving on to it. The other is unlawfully entering or being upon land with any gun, net, engine or other instrument for the purpose of taking or destroying game or rabbits.

Night poachers may be arrested by the police, or apprehended by the owner or occupier of the land, or by his gamekeeper or servant; yet not by the gamekeeper of a sporting tenant, unless he happens to be the owner or occupier of the land. The apprehension may take place either on the spot or, in the event of a pursuit, on any place to which the offender has escaped, and the apprehender may deliver him to the police, who must bring him as soon as may be before two justices of the peace.

The penalty for night poaching is three months' imprisonment for a first offence, six months' for the second, and three years' for the third. Where night poachers gang up in numbers of three or more and are armed with guns, bludgeons or other offensive weapons, the penalty is raised even for the first offence to three years' imprisonment, and a further two may be added for resisting arrest. As with day poachers, the apprehending party may seize and forfeit any game in the possession of the night birds.

Powers of the Police

Until 1960 the powers of a P.C. to pursue and arrest poachers were inconveniently limited. The Game Laws Amendment Act of that year considerably strengthened his hand, by declaring at the outset: " A police constable may arrest a person found on any land ". Indeed, he may enter private property if he suspects that a poacher is on the poach. At night time he may arrest him on the spot. By day he may demand his name and address and order him off the premises; if he disobeys, arrest may follow.

The policeman may also relieve the poacher of any game found in his possession, his gun and ammunition, as well as his " nets, traps, snares and other devices ". If the court convict the miscreant, they may order the game, gun and other devices found on him to be forfeited. If they do not convict, the paraphernalia, or their worth, are given back.

Poaching by farm tenants

Where the game on a farm is reserved, we have seen that the tenant must leave it alone. Although at law he cannot be found guilty of day poaching, he may be fined up to £1 per head of any game he unlawfully kills. Night poaching is another matter, and a tenant caught out in such nocturnal activities, even on his own rented farm, is illegally in the same position as any other poach-by-night.

PART VII

FARMER AND MERCHANT

We introduce this part with a general statement of the law of contract. We then consider some of the special provisions affecting contracts for the sale of goods. Next we deal with three commodities, fertilisers, feedingstuffs and seeds, which the law has singled out for special attention by requiring that certain warranties shall always be given when they change hands. Finally, in view of the enormous increase of interest in recent years in joint buying of requisites and selling of produce, we have included a chapter on the formation of trading groups.

Chapter 31

WHAT MAKES A CONTRACT ?

We have already briefly considered the binding effect of a contract in relation to contracts of service, but here it is necessary to state the rules in rather more detail, for they are the foundation of modern commercial law, applying as much to sales of produce and stock as to sales of industrial products.

Before a binding contract can come into existence the law says that three conditions must be fulfilled. There must be:

(a) an intention to enter into legal relations; and

(b) an unequivocal offer followed by unconditional acceptance; and

(c) consideration, i.e., some element of benefit, however small, on both sides.

Intention to be bound

To tackle these notions one at a time. The first is perhaps the simplest. It must be clear from all the circumstances that the parties intended to create a binding legal relationship. In all ordinary commercial dealings there is no difficulty about this. Life is too short to allow great formality in business, and a brisk exchange of words over the telephone or even an agreement made without the use of speech at all (e.g., at an auction) may result in

An agreement made without the use of speech.

a binding contract. In strict contrast is the so-called gentleman's agreement covering all kinds of " sub-commercial " dealings, or the sportman's agreement with his bookie. Agreements of this sort are unenforceable at law; indeed they are intended to be so. It is the intention of the parties which is the all-important consideration here.

Offer

A great deal has been written and a great many judgments have turned upon the importance of the twin elements of offer and acceptance. A number of colourful and guileless phrases used by business men have found their way to immortality through the Law Reports: " If I hear no more about him, I consider the horse mine at £30 15s."; " A hundred pounds to anyone catching influenza after using one of our Carbolic Smoke Balls three times daily for two weeks "; " We agree to buy Bumper Hall Farm for £900 asked by you. Please send us your title deeds "; and so forth. Such phrases as these have played a vital part in some of the leading cases on offer and acceptance. But though the ingenuity of business men appears to be infinite, the law has dealt in a consistent way with the results of that ingenuity. From the decided cases a number of straightforward and practical rules emerge. First, there must be a clear and unequivocal offer, which must show that the person making the offer intends to be bound by an acceptance. The offer may be made to the world at large or to a specified class or to an individual, and it will ripen into a binding contract at the moment when it is accepted by anyone entitled to do so. The offer may be subject to a time limit; if not it remains open until it has been revoked and the revocation communicated to the offeree. An offer must be carefully distinguished from other commercial statements of a less binding character. For example, a price list or catalogue, or even a price ticket on an article displayed in a shop, does not constitute an offer but merely, as it has been called, " an invitation to treat ". Thus if you go into a bookshop and pick up a book marked £1, you would be wrong to say: " I accept your offer, here is my £1, and I will take the book ". The book may have been reserved for another customer, or the price may have been wrongly stated. The true position is that you have merely been given an invitation to come in and do business. It is you who are making the offer, and it remains for the bookseller to exercise his right to accept or reject it.

Acceptance

Acceptance must be complete in itself and unconditional. " I accept the horse on the understanding that he is sound " would be no acceptance unless the animal had already been warranted sound by the offeror. Acceptance must take the form of some positive act or statement in a manner contemplated by the offeror. For example, if you offer a reward of £10 for information leading to the conviction of anyone committing wilful damage on your farm, it must be within your contemplation that such an offer is likely to be accepted simply by handing over the necessary information. Therefore anyone who knows of the offer is accepting it by giving you the names of the offenders, and there is at that moment a binding contract, subject only to the conviction of the offenders. The £10 becomes payable on conviction, without any further act on the part of the claimant. In contrast, if we make you an offer by telegram: "The old grey mare is yours for £90", we would expect you to reply by the same medium. If you reply by letter this would probably be an insufficient acceptance, and you would have no redress if in the meantime we had sold the old grey mare to someone else. With one important exception it may be said that acceptance must generally be brought to the notice of the offeror. In common fairness it would be unreasonable to expect the owner of, say, a pedigree bull, having offered him to A, to remain constantly under an obligation to A and not to sell him elsewhere. The important exception arises in the case of offers made by post, and depends upon a decision of respectable antiquity, *Henthorn v. Fraser,* 1892. The rule may be summarised as follows:

Where an offer is made by post and in all the circumstances it is reasonable to expect that acceptance will be made by post, then a binding contract comes into existence at the moment when the acceptance is posted. This means in practice that an offeror ought not to assume that his offer has not been accepted at any particular time. It remains open until he has properly revoked it by communicating his revocation to the offeree.

Consideration

This third element in the formation of a contract is not necessary in the case of contracts under seal. But since the vast majority of commercial contracts are made without formality, it may be regarded as one of the essential requirements for our purpose. Consideration presents little difficulty so far as commercial contracts are concerned. Suppose, for example, that A agrees to sell a batch of calves to B at an agreed figure, there is good consideration on both sides because B's promise to pay the purchase price supports A's promise to part with the calves. In the contrasting. case, however, where A agrees to pay his stockman 10s. a head for every calf satisfactorily reared to a certain age, as a bonus over and above what he has already agreed to pay, it is doubtful whether this promise would be legally enforceable, assuming that the stockman was already under a general duty under his contract of service to look after the calves. Consideration must be of some value, but the courts will not inquire into its adequacy. Thus, a nominal 6d. per year might be good consideration for a contractual right to take water from a well or to use a private road.

It has even been held (in *Goddard and Son v. O'Brien,* 1882) that the payment by cheque of £100 would be good consideration for a promise not to sue upon a contract debt of £125. Consideration in this case was the immediate benefit of being paid by cheque, albeit a smaller amount than was originally due under the contract.

It is frequently said that consideration must move from the promisee. This is merely another way of stating the well-known rule that only the parties to a contract can sue on it. If A promises B to confer a benefit on C, the entire arrangement is unenforceable. If, however, a farmer promises a stockbroker to engage his son as a farm pupil, then *provided he agreed to make some payment to the farmer,* the stockbroker would be entitled to sue upon the farmer's promise to take the boy, because the payment which he has agreed to make would be consideration as between himself and the farmer. But the boy himself is not a party to the contract, and could not sue upon it.

In general, contracts which fulfil these conditions will be binding and enforceable. They may be vitiated or rendered unenforceable by all kinds of elements, such as illegality or because one of the parties, for reasons of infancy, lunacy or drunkenness, is legally incapable of making a binding contract. But such difficulties need not detain us here. Perhaps we should mention in passing that certain contracts need to be " evidenced by a note or memorandum in writing ", but the Law Reform (Enforcement of Contracts) Act, 1954, swept away the application of this rule to the contract for the sale of goods to the value of £10 and upwards: the only contracts now affected are bills of exchange and other negotiable instruments, contracts of guarantee, and contracts for the sale of land. Lastly, apart from void contracts, which have no legal effect at all, certain contracts may be rendered voidable, that is to say, they continue to be operative until the party who has a right to avoid their effect has exercised this right. This applies where a party has been induced to contract by fraud, innocent misrepresentation or undue influence.

Chapter 32

SALE OF GOODS

At common law the parties to a contract for the sale of goods were free to make whatever bargain they chose. In the 19th century freedom of contract was treated as a sacred principle in the courts, and such rules as there were merely assisted the courts in arriving at the true intention of the parties at the time of making the contract. The weaknesses of this doctrine will be apparent to anyone who has had occasion to buy, for example, complicated machinery or electrical equipment. So long as the parties stand upon roughly equal ground, they may be expected to arrive at a fair and reasonable bargain of their own accord. For example, two lifelong admirers of that most unpredictable farmyard personality, the pig, might be expected to arrive at a fair price for a nicely mannered maiden gilt of undisputed pedigree. The situa-

A fair price for a nicely mannered maiden gilt.

tion is completely different where, for example, a housewife buys a piece of electrical apparatus or a farmer buys a combine harvester, a chemical herbicide spray, a delicately balanced vitamin feed supplement or any other complex manufactured product, in which he must rely perforce upon the skill of the manufacturer and the good faith of the vendor. In recent years a formidable " consumer protection " movement has grown up, whose main object is to safeguard the public as consumers of industrial or manufactured products, by legislation and by various other means. The Sale of Goods Act, 1893, may be regarded as the first attempt by Parliament to impose a degree of consumer protection upon the common law principle that the parties to a contract are entirely free to make what bargain they please. It brings into play various implied conditions upon the sale of goods of which perhaps the most important are: —

(a) where goods are sold by description, the vendor is presumed under the Act to give a warranty that they are of merchantable quality; and

(b) where goods are sold in circumstances which show that the vendor knows of the purpose to which they are to be put, he may in certain cases be presumed to give a warranty of reasonable fitness for that purpose.

We must now deal with the provisions of the Act in rather more detail.

What are goods ?

The definition of " goods " for the purposes of the Act presents little difficulty. The term is defined as including " all personal chattels other than things in action and money ". In other words, it covers everything, apart from debts and cash, which is movable and capable of legal ownership. But the definition also extends to " emblements, cultivated growing crops and things attached to or forming part of the land which are agreed to be severed before the sale or under the contract of sale ". The insistance upon separation from the land is significant. At common law anything attached to the land is part of the land, and the sale of it would be the sale of an interest in land. The Act, however, takes the practical course and provides that the sale of such bits of " land " must be treated as sales of goods, provided they are to be severed from the land under the contract. In the single case of cultivated crops—as distinct from plants and shrubs which are " the natural growth of the soil "—the Act goes even further and provides that their sale is to be treated as a sale of goods, whether or not there may be any intention to sever them from the land under the contract. To illustrate: if a farmer agrees to sell to a greengrocer " all the apples from the Bramley orchard as soon as they shall have been gathered and weighed by me ", this would be a sale of goods, subject to all the provisions of the 1893 Act. On the other hand, if he agrees to let the local firewood merchant cut and carry away the trees and brushwood in the old spinney over the next seven years, this would not be a sale of goods.

Difficulty occasionally arises over the distinction between a sale of goods and an arrangement with a contractor, for example a plumber, in the course of which the plumber supplies and sells his own materials so far as necessary for the work. It has been held to be a question of fact in each case as to whether the contract is substantially one for the sale of goods or is substantially for services with materials supplied as a convenience.

Passing of the risk

In general the parties may decide for themselves when the risk is to pass, but frequently there is no express agreement about this. If then the goods perish in transit or in the warehouse, the question of liability may have to be determined with the aid of certain rules which the courts have developed to assist them in arriving at the true intention of the parties. For this purpose risk is virtually synonymous with property. The risk passes when the property passes, and upon a sale of specific goods, e.g., the 500 turkeys in the deep freeze, the property passes immediately unless the parties agree to the contrary. If, however, the goods are in an unfinished state at the time of the contract and something remains to be done by the vendor, such as harvesting, separating from the bulk, packing or any kind of processing, the property passes only at the end of the series of acts which the vendor is required to perform in order to give the goods their separate identity for the purposes of the contract. Further, if the vendor has agreed to deliver, the property will pass upon delivery in the absence of agreement to the contrary.

Conditions and warranties

A distinction arose at common law between conditions and warranties in contracts, and this distinction was preserved by the Act of 1893. A condition was regarded as being of the essence of the contract: it is a term of such fundamental importance that the breach of it will entitle the aggrieved party to repudiate the contract at his option. A warranty, on the other hand, whilst it may render the contract more attractive, does not have the same fundamental importance. The breach of a warranty will merely provide the aggrieved party with a right to sue for damages; he will not be entitled to avoid the contract. Whether a term or stipulation in a contract is a condition or a warranty is a question of fact in every case, depending on all the surrounding circumstances. The expressions, " condition " and " warranty " are often used quite loosely; but a warranty will not become a condition simply because the parties have described it as such. Conversely, where an animal is sold as " warranted sound " it may well be that his soundness was really a condition of the contract—not merely a warranty.

Sometimes in spite of a breach of condition the buyer may have accepted and received part of the goods. In such cases the breach must be treated as a breach of warranty only, and the buyer's sole remedy will be in damages. Also it is always open to a party aggrieved by a breach of condition to treat the matter as a breach of warranty only, and to sue for damages instead of avoiding the contract.

Implied terms under the Act

The implied terms, whether they be conditions or warranties, which a vendor is deemed to give fall neatly into two categories: general terms and terms relating to quality. The general terms are three in number. They are first, a condition that the seller has the right to sell—thus, if the seller's title subsequently proves to be defective for any reason the purchaser will be entitled to repudiate the contract. The second implied term is a warranty that the buyer shall have and enjoy quiet possession of the goods. The third is a warranty that the goods are free from any encumbrance or charge.

We now turn to the terms which the Act implies as to the quality of the goods and their fitness for particular purposes. Some of these relate specifically to sales by sample and require:

    (a) that the bulk shall correspond with the sample;

    (b) that the buyer shall have a reasonable opportunity of comparing the bulk with the sample; and

    (c) that the goods are free from any defect which would render them unmerchantable and which would not be apparent on reasonable examination of the sample.

Each of these is a condition whose breach would entitle the puchaser to avoid the contract. Two implied conditions govern sales by description. There is a general condition that the goods shall correspond with the description, and a further condition that where goods are bought by description *from a person who customarily deals in goods of that description*, they shall be of merchantable quality. In practice " merchantable quality " has proved a difficult phrase to construe. In one sense, whether the goods are merchantable depends entirely upon the resource and sagacity of the merchant! This was most certainly not the intention of Parliament, and a forthright and helpful dictum to this effect fell from the judge in *Grant v. Australian Knitting Mills*, 1936, where he said: " Whatever else merchantable may mean, it does mean that the article sold, if only meant for one particular use in the ordinary course, is fit for that use; merchantable does not mean that the thing is saleable in the market simply because it looks all right; it is not merchantable in that event if it has defects unfitting it for its only proper use but not apparent on ordinary examination."

Section 14 (1) of the Act provides that where a buyer shows that he relies on the seller's skill and judgment to provide him with goods fit for a particular purpose, and the goods are such as the seller supplies in the ordinary course of his business, there is an implied condition that the goods shall be fit for that particular purpose. From the point of view of the purchaser this implied

condition is not so useful as it sounds, because it does not apply
to the sale of a product under its patent or trade name. Even
where the article is not sold under a trade name, it may be difficult
for the purchaser, especially if he is accustomed to use goods of
the same general description in his own business, to show that he
relied upon the vendor's skill and judgment. In addition to this
the courts have been somewhat cautious in their interpretation of
section 14 (1), and it has been held that a purchaser cannot rely
upon it if the proposed use for the goods is for something
abnormally sensitive and the vendor is not made aware of this
fact at the time of the sale (*Griffiths v. Conway Limited,* 1936).

Suppose for example that a commercial vegetable grower
declares total war on the red spiders which have been competing
with the plants for occupation of his cucumber houses. The horticultural sundriesman, with whom he has been dealing for the
past 20 years, supplies him with a quantity of " Antimite ", a
chemical preparation said to be capable of dealing effectively with
every known species of red spider. If, having followed the
directions to the letter, the grower finds that the substance has
proved equally lethal to the young plants, he will do well to look
closely at section 14 (1). If he cannot bring himself within it by
showing that he relied upon the expertise of the sundriesman in
selecting this particular product, he will have no redress against
him as a dealer.

Contracting out—" non-warranty " clauses

The Act expressly allows parties to contract out of it. This
provision has been used by manufacturers and distributors alike
to deprive purchasers of such limited rights as they may have
under the Act. Such a case was *L'Estrange v. Graucob Ltd.,* 1934.
A lady who owned a café in Llandudno, had bought on instalments
from the defendants an automatic cigarette machine. She had
signed a " sales agreement " printed on brown paper which read:
" Please forward me as soon as possible a 6 column junior Ilam
Automatic machine. . . . This agreement contains all the terms and
conditions under which I agree to purchase the machine specified
above and any express or implied condition, statement or warranty,
statutory or otherwise, not stated herein is hereby excluded."

The machine proved to be completely useless and defied all
attempts by the firm's mechanic to put it right. Her patience
exhausted, the lady then brought proceedings to recover the instalments she had paid, and after various vicissitudes reached the
Court of Appeal. The court found in favour of the suppliers,
holding the plaintiff to be bound by her express agreement, and
refusing to accept any argument based on the smallness of the
print, or her failure to understand or even to read it.

The case has become something of a charter for those dealers who want to escape the provisions of the Sale of Goods Act, and even the wording of the clause has become painfully familiar. In recent years many judges have frowned upon these dealers' exemption clauses, or " non-warranty " clauses as they are sometimes called. But *L'Estrange v. Graucob Ltd.* is still law, and the courts must give effect to the express terms of the agreement, except in the rare case where the goods are so hopelessly faulty that they do not really satisfy the description of what was ordered.

A case in this exceptional category was *Karsales (Harrow) Ltd. v. Wallis,* 1956, where the Court of Appeal held that a motor-car was in all the circumstances so hopelessly unroadworthy as to be quite unfit for use as a motor-car; therefore the vendors had failed to satisfy what was fundamentally required of them under the contract. In other words, they had failed to deliver anything which would measure up to the ordinary man's conception of what is meant by a " motor-car ", and so were in breach of a fundamental term of the contract. Looked at side by side, the cases are not easy to reconcile, but it will be apparent that the goods must be very seriously defective before the principle of the *Wallis* case can be invoked.

Manufacturers and their " Guarantees "

The manufacturer's guarantee is in a slightly different category from the dealer's exemption clause. The manufacturer is not normally under contract to the final purchaser, the user. He is subject merely to a general common law liability for any foreseeable damage which results from his putting into circulation an article which proves to be dangerous. This common law liability, however—which includes liability for personal injuries—can be nullified by express agreement under a contract. This principle was illustrated in *White v. Warwick and Company Limited,* 1953, which concerned a hiring agreement for a tricycle. The Court of Appeal in that case held that the formula used was not sufficient to relieve the firm from liability for personal injuries suffered by the hirer as a result of a loose saddle, but suggested that a more carefully drafted clause would probably have been effective. Manufacturers, hirers and dealers alike, have been quick to take this hint, and very often guarantees contain a clause to the effect that " no liability is accepted in respect of damage or injury howsoever caused ". The manufacturer cannot avail himself of this kind of exemption clause unless it forms part of an agreement between himself and the person who is going to use the article, and he often secures this by getting the purchaser to sign and return a guarantee form. The purchaser, of course, should read the guarantee form with great care. It may give substantial advantages without corresponding disadvantages from the buyer's point of view. Some guarantees are completely innocuous but these are in the minority. This may appear to be expecting from the purchaser of goods a degree of legal knowledge which the ordinary person may think unreasonable; but the fact remains that the courts expect purchasers to use great care, and under present law the consequences of carelessness of this kind may be serious. The purchaser of agricultural machinery, for example, must be particularly concerned about any possible dangers arising to himself or his workers, and he ought to consider very carefully before signing a guarantee which appears to deprive him of any redress for personal injuries against either the manufacturer or the distributor.

Chapter 33

FERTILISERS, FEEDINGSTUFFS AND SEEDS

These are the three commodities in respect of which Parliament has attempted to protect the farmer as a purchaser from inherent defects which would not be apparent upon ordinary inspection. The provisions relating to these are broadly similar, though there are differences of detail. In each case the seller is required to give

To protect the farmer ... from inherent defects.

a formal statement upon delivery as to the quality and composition of the goods. In each case the statement takes effect as a warranty, and a breach of this statutory warranty *may* render the seller liable to civil proceedings. Furthermore, in the case of all three commodities there are certain acts or omissions which may render the seller liable to criminal proceedings.

FERTILISERS AND FEEDINGSTUFFS

The various provisions affecting sales of fertilisers and feedingstuffs are to be found in the Fertilisers and Feedingstuffs Act, 1926. Life might have been a good deal easier for farmers if it had merely laid down a series of minimum standards for the various commodities. In fact the architects of the Act were primarily concerned not with raising the quality standards of the fertilisers and feedingstuffs trade, but solely with insuring that the purchaser knew what he was getting for his money. To do this it was necessary to sub-divide the various substances into five categories. The

225

five Schedules to the Act in which they are named probably provide the simplest key to the rather complicated provisions of the Act itself. The Minister has power under section 23 to replace or make amendments to any of the Schedules, and this power was exercised in the Fertilisers and Feedingstuffs Regulations, 1960. Schedules I to V of the Regulations therefore replace the five Schedules of the Act, but the differences are differences of detail only.

The Schedules

The First Schedule is a list of fertilisers and feedingstuffs to which all the provisions (both civil and criminal) of the Act apply. The Schedule gives the particulars which must be contained in the statutory statement, to which we shall return. All the commoner substances are to be found in the First Schedule. Part I deals with fertilisers, and the statutory statement in respect of basic slag, for example, is required to give "the total amount of phosphoric acid, the amount of phosphoric acid soluble in citric acid and the amount of the article that will pass through a prescribed sieve". Part II deals with feedingstuffs and, again to select one item at random, in the case of compound cakes or meals the statutory statement is required to give the amounts of oil, protein and fibre respectively.

The Second Schedule is a list of articles to which some only of the provisions of the Act are applicable. Like the First, this Schedule also gives the particulars required to be contained in the statutory statement; but these are effective for civil purposes only and a breach will not constitute a criminal offence.

The Third Schedule lists substances commonly considered to be of negligible feeding value. These are not prohibited, but their presence in feedingstuffs must be declared. The list includes such items as husks, chaff, nutshells or skins of nuts, peat, spent hops, wheat or rye straw, and sawdust.

The Fourth Schedule gives a list of the definitions to be "implied on the sale of articles under certain names". Again this is in two parts, for fertilisers and for feedingstuffs, and like the First Schedule it is effective for civil and criminal purposes. Thus basic slag is defined as "a by-product, containing phosphorus, obtained in the manufacture of steel and to which no addition has been made at the time of leaving or after it has left the furnace". Similarly, barley meal is defined as "the meal obtained by grinding barley, as grown, which shall be the whole grain together with only such other substances as may reasonably be expected to have become associated with the grain in the field and which contains not less than 96 per cent pure barley".

The Fifth Schedule deals with "deleterious ingredients in feedingstuffs". This is to be read in connection with section 7, which provides that it is an offence to sell or expose for sale feedingstuffs containing any of the listed ingredients. The Schedule raises serious problems of interpretation, and it is not easy to say in advance that the presence of any particular toxic element in a feedingstuff would constitute an offence. The list includes "all poisonous substances except those naturally present in the material or materials from which the feedingstuff is derived". It is well known, for example, that castor seed may be toxic if taken in sufficient quantity, though it may also be a very desirable ingredient in compounds. Some help may be derived from the definitions clause suggesting that the standard to be applied is that of the "average commercial sample".

It will have been noted that Schedules III and V relate to feedingstuffs only, while Schedules I, II and IV are in two parts and relate to both commodities.

Effect of the statutory statement

The statutory statement is chiefly of value in creating a warranty which can, if necessary, be relied upon in civil proceedings. The Act further provides that if any voluntary additional statement is made this also will take effect as a warranty. This would apply, for example, to statements about the actual ingredients of a feedingstuff or to statements about the fineness of grinding in the case of a fertiliser.

The statutory definitions contained in the Fourth Schedule also give rise to a form of warranty, and an aggrieved buyer would be entitled to rely upon any failure to comply with the definition in civil proceedings.

The effect of an inaccuracy in the statutory statement is interesting. In *Anderson v. Daniel*, 1923, the Court of Appeal held that a seller of fertiliser who omitted without a reasonable excuse to give a statutory statement would not be entitled to recover the unpaid purchase price for the goods. In other words, the court treated the contract as an illegal one and therefore void. The case was decided under the Act of 1906, but the Act of 1926 provides in section 1 (2) that failure to give the statutory statement "shall not invalidate a contract for sale". Thus under present law, if the seller fails to provide any statement at all, or the statement contains information which subsequently proves to be inaccurate, the buyer has no right to treat the contract as being at an end. He will remain liable for the purchase price but he may be entitled to damages for breach of warranty. This right of action will arise even though the contract may contain some express provision which might appear to rule this out. This is because section 2 of the 1926 Act provides that the statutory statement shall take effect as a written warranty "notwithstanding any contract or notice to the contrary". In this respect the statutory warranties provided here are stronger than those contained in the Sale of Goods Act, because in this instance there is no right of contracting out.

Enforcement

The administration of the Act is primarily the responsibility of County Councils and County Boroughs. They must appoint official agricultural analysts, inspectors and samplers. The Act and Regulations contain elaborate provisions about the procedure for sampling and analysis, and the sampling must take place not on the farm but on the seller's premises. In dealing with the Schedules we have already mentioned that certain breaches of the provisions of the Act, in addition to giving rise to civil claims, may also constitute criminal offences. In the case of most of the offences, however, the consent of the Minister of Agriculture is needed before a prosecution can take place.

Sampling and analysis in accordance with the detailed steps laid down in the Act and the 1960 Regulations are relevant only for the purposes of a prosecution. In the case of a civil claim there is no reason why the purchaser should not rely entirely upon analysis by a private analyst. If, however, the consignment is so grossly defective that the buyer discovers the trouble in time, he is entitled to make use of the statutory procedure for sampling and analysis, provided that he does so within 14 days. There is a special defence available to sellers in a prosecution for false marking, giving false particulars or omitting to state the presence of a worthless ingredient. If the seller can prove justifiable ignorance of the facts which constitute the offence, he is entitled to be acquitted, provided that if he obtained the article from someone else, he makes available to the prosecutor "all the information he has about its origin".

SEEDS

Transactions in seeds are governed mainly by the Seeds Act, 1920, and the Seeds Regulations, 1961. These require all sellers of the principal kinds of agricultural and vegetable seeds to give the customers certain information, contained in a "statutory statement". First, there is one general requirement applying to all sales of seeds: that the seller must give his name and address as part of this statutory statement. Apart from this general rule, the information to be included in the statutory statement is dealt with in the Regulations, and the contents of the statement may vary from one group of seeds to another. The main headings under which information must be given are: —

(a) purity;

(b) germination;

(c) freedom from injurious weed seeds;

(d) variety; and

(e) country of origin.

Seed potatoes are in a special category. Here the seller has to give the reference numbers and letters of the certificate (assuming they are certified), also the class, the variety, the size and dressing. Where any seeds, including seed potatoes, have been treated with a liquid or powder to control pests or diseases, or have been fumigated, this fact has to be included in the statement.

The Regulations

The Regulations of 1961 made considerable extensions in the varieties of seeds covered. The agricultural seeds are classified in four groups. The first is herbage seed, which now includes varieties like Westerwold's ryegrass, tall and red fescue, meadow foxtail, suckling clover and yarrow. The second is cereal seeds, in which maize (excluding sweet corn) has been added to the original quartet—wheat, barley, oats and rye. The third class comprises field seeds of various kinds, including flax, linseed, lupin and sunflower. The fourth and largest category consists of the root and vegetable seeds, ranging from the essentials of life like mangel and kale to luxuries such as endive and celeriac.

All these are covered and dealt with in one way or another by the Act. The declaration of variety or type is required in virtually every case for agricultural and horticultural seeds, and a declaration of the country of origin for all seeds except packeted root and vegetable seeds. A declaration as to percentage germination is required for all the listed seeds, and a declaration of analytical purity for everything except cucumber, melon and vegetable marrow.

There is an absolute prohibition on the sale of any seed containing more than 5 per cent by weight of certain injurious weeds. But no declaration is needed in the case of seeds in general in the statutory statement where smaller quantities of weed seeds may be present. Under the 1961 Regulations the percentage of weed seeds of all kinds has to be declared in herbage, field and cereal seeds if over $0 \cdot 5$ per cent. A declaration has also to be made about the content of certain injurious weeds if above a specified quantity. These injurious weeds include wild oat, docks and sorrels, and couch grass.

Effect of the statutory statement

With respect to civil liability, the statutory statement takes effect as a qualified warranty. In view of the strict rules which the Act says a dissatisfied purchaser must follow, the value of the statement as establishing the conditions of sale between the parties is seriously reduced. Section 6 (1) of the Act provides that in any legal proceedings on a contract for the sale of seeds "the particulars contained in the statement delivered in pursuance of this Act on the sale shall be *deemed to be true* unless it is made to appear on a test made subject to the provisions of this section that the particulars were untrue". A dissatisfied purchaser must, within 10 days of delivery of the seed or the statement, whichever is the later, take a sample of the delivered seed, divide it, and send part to the seller and the rest to the official seed testing station. Failure to take these formal steps will leave him without a remedy under the Act. From this it will be apparent that, unless the consignment of seed is so seriously defective that the purchaser's suspicions are aroused within the period allowed for sampling, he will have no civil claim against the vendor, even though it may subsequently be possible to prove that the delivered seed fails to comply with the statutory statement. There may be farmers who religiously go through the procedure of taking a sample from every parcel of seed they buy; but if so we have not met them.

Thus the seed merchant is virtually free from civil responsibility for the sale after the 10-day period has elapsed. If he has failed to take the formal steps the farmer will have no right to reject the seed and reclaim the purchase money, nor will he have any right to bring any action for damages in the event of a crop failure arising from some defect in the seed. Notwithstanding the favourable position which they enjoy under the Act, most merchants find it desirable also to impose conditions upon the following lines: —

" We guarantee that all seeds offered or sold by us to which the Seeds Act, 1920, and the Regulations made thereunder apply have been tested in accordance with the provisions of the same. In accordance with the established custom of the seed trade, we give no other guarantee. It is therefore not a condition of sale, neither do we warrant, expressly or impliedly by or under the terms of the Sale of Goods Act, 1893, or any other statute or enactment, that the seeds supplied shall correspond with the description under which they are sold, or be fit for any particular purpose, or free from injurious or latent defect such as loose smut disease of wheat, and we will not be responsible for the crop. The giving of an order constitutes an acceptance of these terms by the purchaser who, if he does not accept these terms, must return the goods forthwith."

The effect of these conditions by the seller, in the words of the Report of the Committee on Transactions in Seeds, 1957, is that " a purchaser of seed is not entitled to rely on a misstatement of any of the statutory particulars in any civil proceedings he may wish to bring against the seller ".

Enforcement

The Act and Regulations are the responsibility of the Ministry of Agriculture, which is also the authority responsible for the prosecution of offences committed under the Act, such as the failure to deliver any statutory statement at all or the making of a statutory statement which is " false in any material particular ". The offences created by the Act may be dealt with summarily (i.e., before the magistrates), and are punishable by small fines between £5 and £20. For seed potatoes proceedings may be brought at any time within 12 months from the date on which the alleged offence was committed—this notwithstanding the general rule that proceedings for summary offences must be brought within six months.

There is an official seed testing station established under the Act, situated at Cambridge, to which samples have to be sent for the testing of purity, germination and weed content. Merchants are permitted however to operate their own stations for the testing of seeds which they have purchased or intend to sell. These stations may be operated under licence of the Ministry, and are subject to control and supervision to insure that the apparatus and methods conform to official requirements. Inspectors are also authorised by the Minister to visit seedsmen's premises to take samples of seeds which are there exposed for sale; and official check tests are made to insure that the particulars being declared by the seller are correct.

Chapter 34

FARMING PARTNERSHIPS

In view of the number of partnerships to be found in agriculture —more perhaps than in any other business—it seems appropriate to include a chapter outlining partnership law. That the chapter is short should not disguise the fact that the subject is intricate. Disputes of surprising length and complexity have arisen from the simplest, most informal of family partnership agreements.

Informal ... partnership agreements.

The nature of partnership

Partnership law is dominated almost entirely by the Partnership Act, 1890. The Act is largely declaratory, that is to say, it is used as a guide to the intentions of the parties where they are inadequately expressed, while allowing the parties in most respects to vary their rights and duties, as between themselves, by express contrary agreement. A partnership is defined in section 1 of the Act as " the relation which subsists between persons carrying on business in common with a view of profit ". The basis of a partnership must be some form of agreement, but it need not be in writing: it may even be inferred from an habitual course of dealing. Partnership is to be distinguished from co-ownership of property, which does not of itself constitute partnership, and vice versa.

A father's ownership of his farm, buildings and livestock is not affected by taking a son into partnership, unless he expressly agrees that the farm is to become partnership property. Similarly if, later on, father and son decide to acquire a second farm out of the profits of the partnership, the second farm will belong to them as co-owners merely, and will not become part of the partnership property unless they make an express agreement to this effect.

In general the ordinary rules of contract apply to the formation of a partnership. No particular form is required for the partnership agreement, which may be by word of mouth, but there are one or two pitfalls to be avoided. An important one is that a partnership consisting of more than 20 persons becomes illegal under the Companies Act, 1948. There are also some restrictions upon the choice of the partnership name. In general the parties have a fair measure of freedom to select the firm name, subject to three conditions: —

(a) the word "limited" may not be used (section 439 of the Companies Act, 1948);

(b) the name must be registered under the Registration of Business Names Act, 1916, if it does not consist of the true surnames of all the partners, or if any partner has changed his name; and

(c) a competitor may restrain the use of a misleading name by means of an injunction for "passing off" if the public is likely to believe that it is in fact dealing with the competitor.

Partnership trading

Every partner has a kind of implied agency to enter into ordinary business transactions on behalf of the firm. The firm will be bound to honour transactions entered into by any partner within the ordinary course of the firm's business. Thus, in a farming partnership one partner, in an unguarded moment at the Royal Show, might allow himself to be talked into ordering a gargantuan quantity of hormone spray. The firm will be liable unless the quantity ordered is so enormous that it could not conceivably be used in the ordinary course of cultivations on one farm; in which case the partner placing the order will be liable personally upon the contract.

Quite apart from liability for its contracts, a partnership may as a firm incur liability in tort. Clearly the partnership will be liable for the torts of the firm. Suppose, for example, that Messrs. W. & F. Jones, Fruit Growers, of Windfall Fruit Farm, have been counting the dwindling returns from sales of top fruit in the local town for the past five years or more. One day whilst strolling in the market place, F. Jones happens to see scrawled in chalk about four feet up from the ground the words "Jones's Windfalls". The penny drops, and in less than no time the Joneses are sending in load after load of apples and pears in brand-new boxes labelled SUNBLEST TOP FRUIT—and in tiny letters underneath: " W. & F. Jones, sole proprietors ". The profits pour in for about a year; then one morning a letter arrives from a firm of London solicitors acting as agents for the New York lawyers of the " Sunblest Top Fruit Corporation of the U.S.A." The American firm will be entitled to an award of damages against the partnership, but only if they can show that the Joneses have " passed off " their goods as the company's goods by imitating the form or get-up of the company's product, and that the company has suffered loss thereby.

Apart from torts jointly committed by the partners, the partnership may also be liable for torts committed by one partner under the implied agency of the firm. Thus, in a firm of farmer-cattle-dealers, all the partners will be liable to account to a third party for any cattle belonging to the third party received and privately misappropriated by one of the partners. The liability in tort is " joint and several ", which means that not only will all the partners be jointly liable but each of them will be liable for the full amount if the others' default. In contrast, liability for the contractual debts of the partnership is merely a joint liability, and the partners will be liable in the proportions in which they normally share profits.

As between themselves, the relationship of the partners has much in common with the obligation of a servant to his master (discussed at page 98). A partner is bound to account to the firm for any private profit which he may make in the course of the firm's business. The Partnership Act goes further than this and provides, in sections 28 and 29, that a partner is bound to render true accounts and full information on all matters affecting the firm; he must also account to the firm for any benefit derived by him from any transaction concerning the partnership or from the use of the firm property, name or connection. In the profits and losses of the firm, all the partners are presumed to be entitled to share equally, irrespective of their capital contributions, unless the partnership agreement otherwise provides. In general a partner is at liberty to assign his share in the partnership to someone else, but that person does not necessarily become a partner. He merely becomes entitled to a share in the profits. If one partner's share becomes subject to a charging order in respect of a debt owed privately by that partner, the other partners may either: —

(a) redeem the share by paying off the charge;

(b) purchase the share if the court orders the sale of it; or

(c) dissolve partnership by service of notice.

Chapter 35

JOINT TRADING VENTURES

In recent years there has been a remarkable toughening of the commercial world which nudges the farmer at both ends of his productive process. He finds that the raw materials, tools, and machinery which he has to buy are controlled by increasingly powerful commercial companies and groups; whilst at the marketing end he finds similar concentrations of commercial power in the food industry, which can make his life very difficult in the case of non-price review commodities, where his rewards are strictly limited to what his produce can make in a " free " market. In the buying of requisites as well as on the selling side, the farmer, no matter how large his acreage may be, is ever a small man doing battle with giants. Against this background it is scarcely surprising that purchasing and marketing are now frequently looked upon as functions quite separate from the management of the farm. The optimum size of a farm is subject to practical limitations. The business side of the farmer's activities should be at least big enough to talk to " the British Basic Slag Corporation " and " Nationwide Supermarkets Limited " in language which can readily be understood.

A remarkable toughening of the commercial world.

Ways and means

There may be a stage in the life of any business association or partnership when it becomes desirable that the partners should merge their business completely and seek incorporation as a company. Whatever the business of the company, two advantages follow automatically from its creation. First, the company is a separate legal person which may sue and be sued in its own name, subject to fixed upper limits of liability usually with reference to share capital. The second is that a company is, at least potentially, immortal. This may strike a hollow note in these days of the " take-over bid ", when companies once thought to be invincible may be gobbled up like minnows overnight. As we shall see, however, many companies are virtually immune from take-over, and in any event it may be desirable that the lifetime of a business enterprise should be longer than the lives or terms of office of individuals. These two features of incorporation—limited liability and continuity—become virtually indispensable when a number of farmers merge their trading activities. Where more than 20 people resolve to carry on some trading activity in association with one another, incorporation becomes a legal necessity by virtue of section 434 of the Companies Act, 1948. It is unlawful for an association of this size to carry on a trading venture with a view to profit; but even smaller associations will run into serious practical difficulties unless they seek the benefit of incorporation at an early stage.

There are two quite separate procedures whereby a joint trading venture may become incorporated and so acquire the benefit of a distinct legal personality. Certain features are common to both types, but the approach may vary according to the nature of the project and the amount of capital required. Thus incorporation may be achieved either: —

(a) by registration as a co-operative society under the Industrial Provident Societies Acts, 1893 to 1961; or

(b) by registration as a company under the Companies Act, 1948.

Basic rules for co-operatives

The term " co-operative " has no distinct meaning in English law, but some guidance is given by the Prevention of Fraud (Investments) Act, 1939. The Act empowers the Registrar of Friendly Societies to refuse registration to any society which does not appear to him to be a bona fide co-operative society. A bona fide society does not include " a society which carries on or intends to carry on business with the object of making profits mainly for the payment of interest, dividends or bonuses on money invested or deposited with or lent to the society ". The Registrar has a wide discretion to refuse registration but, of course, he normally acts within the well-established principles developed for the guidance of industrial and provident societies. To indicate how his discretion may be exercised, the Registrar has published a five-point memorandum, which we reproduce here.

" The Act does not define a bona fide Co-operative Society, but the nature of such a Society may be indicated in a general way by the following observations:

(a) An investment Society as defined in subsection (9) is expressly excluded, i.e., a Society which is carried on with the object of making profits mainly for the payment of interest on money invested with or through the Society.

(b) The Society must so conduct its business as to show that its main purpose is the mutual benefit of its members, and that the benefit enjoyed by a member depends upon the use which he makes of the facilities provided by the Society and not upon the amount of money which he invests in the Society. In the case of such Societies as Agricultural Co-operative Societies, although the member may be required to take up shares in proportion to the amount of his land or stock, etc., the Society nevertheless exists primarily to provide benefits for the member in proportion to the use which he makes of the marketing or other facilities furnished by the Society.

(c) There must be no artificial restriction of membership with the object of increasing the value of proprietary rights or interests. On the other hand there may be reasons for restricting membership which would not offend the co-operative principle, e.g., a club's membership may be limited by the size of its premises; a Society may confine its activities to a particular class of persons or to a particular area. By contrast, if the membership were limited in order to give the maximum benefit to a restricted number of persons the Society might not be regarded as truly co-operative.

(d) A rule providing that any persons should have more than one vote might suggest prima facie that the Society was not a true Co-operative Society.

(e) The return on share and other capital must not exceed a moderate rate which may vary according to circumstances but should be approximate to the minimum necessary to obtain such capital as is required to carry out the primary objects of the Society." (At present 1 per cent above Bank Rate or 5 per cent per annum, whichever is the higher.)

Co-operative Societies

The Co-operative Society is a refinement of the old mutual benefit societies, or friendly societies, which began to flourish in the early part of the last century. The Friendly Societies Acts of the middle 1800's were passed in order to give them a definite legal

framework within which to operate, and in 1846, a salaried registrar was appointed whose function it was, and still is, to exercise
a benevolent supervision over their formation and activities. From
the original function of providing benefits and various services
for the help of their members, the societies gradually turned their
attention to wider possibilities and, with the passing of the first
Industrial and Provident Societies Act in 1852, they were enabled
to invest the savings of members for certain limited purposes. In
the picturesque language of the time, they were entitled as one of
their objects to carry out " the frugal investment of savings of
their members for better enabling them to purchase food, firing,
clothes and other necessaries or the tools and implements of their
trade or calling ".

By 1876, when the first complete and independent code for
industrial and provident societies emerged in the form of a consolidating Act, they had already acquired the safeguard of limited
liability. In the new legislation the principles of co-operation
were adapted to the notion of a trading society, and many of the
rules then laid down remain fully effective today. The Act of
1876 provided that the rate of interest on capital should be limited
to 5 per cent; that audited accounts were to be prepared twice
yearly and submitted to the Registrar; that shareholding was to
be limited to a fixed sum for each member; that the liability of
members should be limited; and it legalised the payment of
dividends on purchases which had already been carried on in
practice for a number of years.

Despite many changes of detail, there have been few alterations
of these basic principles. The maximum permitted investment
now stands at £1,000 for each member under the Industrial and
Provident Societies Act, 1961. There is no such limit upon the
capital which may be invested in a limited company, this being
perhaps the most important distinction between the two systems
of registration. Under present law there is no substantial difference
between the trading powers of the two sorts of co-operative. Both
the society and the company may make contracts through their
officers for any of the purposes permitted by their " objects ".

Producer companies

Let us now suppose that a group of fruit growers in the Vale
of Thrift have met and decided to put an end to competing with
one another to sell strawberries to the trade at knock-down prices.
If their sole objective is the marketing of produce in bulk, with
perhaps a little bulk buying of requisites for good measure, a
society on the co-operative pattern may ideally suit their purpose.
The sacred principle of " one man, one vote " provides the best
possible guarantee of democratic control, whilst the restrictions
upon share transfer give virtually complete protection against the

possibility of take-over. The Vale of Thrift Growers' Society Limited might well be able to do valiant service to its members and establish itself as a successful marketing venture without the aid of a great deal of capital. Yet suppose, for the sake of contrast, that the Association of Scottish Beef Producers resolve to form an ambitious marketing organisation to bridge the enormous gulf between the Aberdeen-Angus and the housewife. It will be seen immediately that quite different commercial and legal considerations have to be satisfied. The organisation, if it is to be commercially effective, will need (either from the beginning or in the fullness of time) its own slaughterhouses, cold stores and transport, together with all the paraphernalia of its own advertising and distribution system. As applied to an organisation of this kind, the co-operative pattern has several grave legal disadvantages. Probably the chief of these are:—

(a) the limitations upon capital invested; and

(b) the direct system of democratic control enshrined in the principle of "one member, one vote", which may be a distinct commercial disadvantage in competing with " the established trade ", where decisions of commercial policy may be taken swiftly and without recourse to democratic procedures.

Most farmers' trading projects will fall somewhere between the two extremes which we have just outlined, and we do not propose to explore in detail the relative merits or disadvantages of limited companies as opposed to co-operative societies. The fact remains, however, that in recent years a number of such projects have taken the form of limited companies, we will offer therefore, in a few short paragraphs, the main outlines of company law as applied to this form of commercial development.

The law regards the registered company as merely a special type of corporation. Thus, the commercial company is governed almost entirely by the Companies Act, 1948; but the concept of incorporation goes back much further into our legal history; indeed, the earliest companies were created by charter. From time to time specially privileged bodies like the British Broadcasting Corporation and the British Overseas Airways Corporation have been directly incorporated by special Acts of Parliament, but such companies are comparatively rare. The common feature which all these bodies share—and this is the basis of company law—is that as companies they are separate legal persons; separate, that is, from the individuals who compose them. Their ability to do business, and in particular to make contracts, is defined by reference to certain fixed rules, while the liability of their members for the acts of the company may be limited in certain ways.

For the modern commercial company, the Companies Act of 1948 is at once father, mother and midwife. It permits of two

main types of company, public or private. The distinction is an
easy one, because section 28 lays down that a *private* company
must:—

(a) restrict the right to transfer its shares;

(b) limit the number of members of the company to 50
(excluding employees and past employees of the company);
and

(c) prohibit any invitation to the public to subscribe for shares
or debentures.

Any company not complying with these conditions will be a
public company. In general the private company is usually considered most appropriate for agricultural trading. It may well
be desirable to take advantage of the privilege of not having to
include a balance sheet in the annual return to the Registrar of
Companies. The Registrar has functions comparable to those of
the Registrar of Friendly Societies, and the exemption from return-
ing a balance sheet is granted to private companies who can show
that they are not partially or wholly owned or controlled by other
companies or persons who are not members of the company. The
limitation upon membership may involve difficulties if a large
amount of capital is required for trading purposes, but the Act
of 1948 provides for the conversion by democratic process of a
private company into a public company, with power to invite
public investment or investment by any section of the public, and
such conversions are relatively common. Another advantage of a
private company is that it may begin trading immediately after
incorporation.

The trading powers of a company are defined in the objects
clause of the document known as the " Memorandum of Association ". Another document, " The Articles of Association ", also
has to be filed with the Registrar at the time the company is
registered. Together these contain the whole of the company's
constitution, in much the same way as the constitution of a
friendly society is governed by its rules. Broadly speaking, the
Memorandum deals with essentials like the objects and where
the company is to carry on business, whilst the Articles deal
with the structure of the company and such matters as the appointment of directors and the restrictions upon share transfer or
membership, if any. The importance of the objects clause lies in
the legal doctrine of " ultra vires ". Generally speaking the company will be incapable of making contracts outside the scope of
its objects clause, a fact which has led to the modern fashion of
drafting objects clauses extremely widely.

The liability of members of the company may be limited by two
alternative methods, either (a) by shares, or (b) by guarantee. If

the company is limited by shares, the liability of members is limited to the face value of their individual shareholdings. Similarly if the the company is limited by guarantee, the liability of each member is limited to the amount which he has agreed or guaranteed to pay in the event of the company's insolvency. Share capital may perhaps be thought an indispensable prerequisite for a trading company, but at least one company limited by guarantee has been flourishing in the field of agricultural marketing for a number of years. The explanation is the use of borrowed capital, in which case the interest upon the loan or loans will be a charge upon the company's trading activities. The return to the members upon the company's profits may take the form of a bonus based on through-put; it may even take the form of enhanced prices or better services. Amongst ordinary commercial companies, however, trading substantially upon borrowed capital must be regarded as the exception. The use of investment capital, whether or not it involves the distribution of some of the profits in the form of dividends on shares, is the general rule.

PART VIII

RATES AND TAXES

Many times we have heard it rashly and enviously asserted that " farmers pay no rates ". It is true that farm land and buildings were derated as long ago as 1929, but rating authorities have always regarded this privilege through narrowed eyes, and the limits imposed by case law upon agricultural rating relief have had some surprising practical results.

In this, the last part of our book, we consider the farmer first as a ratepayer, then as a taxable subject.

PART VIII

RATES AND TAXES

Chapter 36
GENERAL PRINCIPLES OF RATING LAW

Modern rating law finds its statutory basis in the Poor Relief Act, 1601. In the hallowed words of the Act " every occupier of lands, houses . . . and saleable underwoods " was liable to contribute to the rate. "Occupier " is the key word, and to this day it is the occupation (not the ownership) of land or buildings which

Every occupier . . . was liable to contribute to the rate.

carries the liability to pay rates. The collection of the rate, in each of the 15,000 parishes in England and Wales, was the responsibility of the Overseers of the Poor; but the Overseers were also the spending authorities—a combination of functions not regarded as entirely healthy by modern political theorists!

Local government services were gradually extended to other and more complex fields. By the end of the 19th century public health, education and housing had become the primary functions. Local authorities had taken on a form not very different from their appearance today, but rating was still based on the parish unit. In Gloucestershire, in 1881, a 200-acre farm was in 12 different rating areas and subject to about 50 different rates.

Rationalisation came with the Rating and Valuation Act, 1925. The modern authorities—County Boroughs, Borough Councils, Rural and Urban District Councils—then became the rating authorities. Uniformity was achieved by providing that in all rating areas there must be one consolidated rate, called " the general rate ", at a uniform amount per £ on the rateable value of each hereditament. The old method of demand and recovery of rates continued in force, and indeed remains in force today.

One further refinement was introduced under the Local Government Act of 1948. This did not affect the function of the rating authority as being responsible for collection. The preparation of the valuation lists, however, became the function of the Inland Revenue Department.

Although assigned to a central government department, this function in practice is delegated to the department's local officers— the District Rating and Valuation Officers, to give them their full title; and these officials consequently have a dual responsibility both to a rating authority and to the Valuation Office of the Inland Revenue.

The nature of rateable occupation

In the Act of 1601 the word " occupiers " is not defined. Consequently we are forced to rely entirely upon case law for guidance as to what kind of occupation gives rise to the liability for rates.

There are traditionally four ingredients of rateable occupation, and these four ingredients must all be present. There must be actual possession; the occupation must be beneficial, and exclusive, and not merely transient.

To take these one at a time; first, actual or *"de facto"* possession. Here ownership is entirely irrelevant. The essence is some " overt act of occupation ", such as the cultivation of land or the regular use of buildings. A building which is not used at all is not rateable, but buildings which are temporarily empty may be rateable. The test here is whether the emptiness or non-user is in some way contributing to the value of the land or buildings. For example, although it would be in the nature of a warehouse, boarding house or even the gathering grounds of a reservoir not to be in use at certain seasons, yet in each case these have been held to be rateable, though not directly in use.

The occupation must be " beneficial ". This means that it must be one which would command a rent. A good deal of confusion has arisen from this, because the meaning of beneficial in this sense does not necessarily involve profitability. Thus business premises may be of value even though the business is running at a loss, and it has indeed been held that an unprofitable business may be rateable.

The occupation must be exclusive. This means that the occupier must be in a position to exclude all others from using the property. It does not mean that he must necessarily do so. For example, the rateable occupier of display cabinets in a railway station has been held to be the railway company. This is because the company, and it alone, can control entry and egress from the station. In contrast to this, however, it has been held that the rateable occupier of tramlines is the tramway company, though clearly the company could not restrain access to the highway. Gas mains have been held to be rateable as being in the exclusive occupation of the gas undertaking.

Lastly, in addition to being exclusive, the occupation must not be merely transient. In other words there must be some degree of permanence; therefore the occupation of land for a few days by circus sideshows or by caravans would not be rateable.

Competing occupancies

In some cases more than one person may be in apparent occupation of the same premises. The tied cottage and the tied public house are both good examples of this. The agricultural worker and the public house manager respectively have the physical occupation of the premises; but the farmer or the brewery company have general control of the use of the premises inasmuch as the occupation by the employee is tied to his contract of service. The House of Lords has laid down the test to be applied to establish rateable occupation in such cases. The court or tribunal must ask " which party is in paramount occupation? " If the landlord has control, then the landlord is the rateable occupier. In the case of a farm cottage, if the occupier is a service occupier, so that the farmer has control, then the farmer is the rateable occupier.

The effect of this rule upon rateable values is significant. If the rateable occupier were the farm worker, it might be, because he is entitled by virtue of the wages legislation to occupation of the cottage in consideration of a statutory deduction of 6s. per week only, that 6s. should be taken as representing the reasonable rent for the purpose of ascertaining the rateable value. This was strongly argued in *Bomford v. South Worcestershire Assessment Committee,* 1947. But it was held that, applying the principle of paramount occupation, the real rateable occupier was the farmer. To the farmer the cottage might be worth considerably more than the statutory 6s. per week, and in the circumstances a higher rateable value could be fixed.

Although in the case of a tied cottage the rateable occupation, and therefore the liability to pay rates, will usually be upon the farmer, the farmer may pass on the rate burden to the worker under the service agreement. But we have already seen at page

104 that the Wages Orders make provision for this. In calculating the minimum wage, the maximum deduction for the cottage under the Orders is 6s. (or such other sum as may be fixed by a County Wages Committee), including rates if paid by the worker.

Rating of owners

In law, then, liability for rates is based on occupation. In practice, however, where a number of cottages and small houses are let to tenants it may be a considerable administrative inconvenience to collect rates from individual occupiers. Accordingly, quite apart from rules of paramount occupation, in order to relieve rating authorities from the expense which would otherwise be involved, the Rating and Valuation Act, 1925, provided that rating authorities might in certain circumstances be given power to collect rates from owners. This involves making what is known as a " compounding resolution ". It has the effect of a direction that in the case of properties of a certain class (classified by rateable value) the owners and not the occupiers will be rateable. This power at present applies to properties whose rateable value did not exceed £18 in 1955.

Apart from their powers to make compounding resolutions, rating authorities may also enter into compounding agreements with individual owners. These agreements when made have the same effect, but there is no limit on the rateable value of the property which may be affected. In either case the authority may make a compounding allowance, which takes the form of a rebate of up to 15 per cent.

Calculation of rateable values

Although the valuation of property for rating purposes has come to be regarded as a highly specialised mystique, the governing principles are clearly laid down by statute. The gross value, from which the rateable value is derived is, according to the Rating and Valuation Act, 1925, the rent at which the hereditament might reasonably be expected to let from year to year if the landlord undertook to bear the cost of repairs and insurance. Deductions are then made in accordance with a statutory scale to give a net annual value. This figure, the net annual value, is the rateable value for most types of property, including dwelling-houses.

The Act of 1925 provided for a revaluation on a national scale of all rateable property at five-yearly intervals. The third such revaluation was postponed on account of the war, and finally took effect on the 1st April, 1956. Property was then revalued for rating purposes, subject to an important qualification contained in the Valuation for Rating Act, 1953. Certain rateable values were, by virtue of the provisions of the 1953 Act, artificially depressed to the level of 1939 rents. The properties affected were dwelling-houses, private garages and private storage premises; for these the gross value was to be based on the " rent at which the hereditament might reasonably have been expected to let from year to year, etc." in 1939. Under the Rating and Valuation Act, 1961, however, these are restored to a current letting value basis as from 1st April, 1963.

Procedure

In fixing rateable values, it is normally the rating officer who takes the initiative by making a formal " proposal ". If the occupier objects either to the valuation or to the inclusion of the hereditament in the valuation list, he must object in writing in 28 days. The objection is then heard by the Local Valuation Court, consisting of selected members of a valuation panel of magistrates. Appeals from the decision of the court may be made, on questions of valuation or law, to the Lands Tribunal, that same tribunal which deals with compulsory purchase matters (page 141). Further appeal lies to the Court of Appeal, but on points of law only.

The above procedure applies to the ordinary case where the rating officer makes a proposal for an alteration in the valuation list. In the event of a change of circumstances or of use, the ratepayer may wish to make a proposal, for example, to delete from the valuation list a building which has become an agricultural building. In this event the ratepayer and the valuation officer merely exchange roles, the ratepayer making the initial proposal.

Chapter 37

AGRICULTURAL RATING RELIEF

Many kinds of hereditaments are fully or partially relieved from the duty to pay rates. This relief can only arise by statute, and the statutory provisions as to derating which have accumulated over the years deal with a wide variety of premises. Of these by far the most important are agricultural land and buildings which were totally derated by the Local Government Act, 1929.

Totally derated by the Local Government Act, 1929.

Agricultural land

The definition of agricultural land and buildings for this purpose is to be found in section 2 (2) of the Rating and Valuation (Apportionment) Act, 1928. " Agricultural land " is there defined as " land used as arable, meadow or pasture ground only . . . land exceeding a quarter of an acre used for poultry farming . . . market gardens, nursery grounds, orchards or allotments ". The definition expressly excludes " land occupied together with a house as a park " and " land kept or preserved mainly or exclusively for purposes of sport or recreation ".

Perhaps the most significant word in this definition of land is " only ", which appears to govern the first part of the definition.

This has led to a number of cases in which agricultural land has been rated because the occupier has embarked upon some enterprise unconnected with agriculture. For example, it has been held that land used for turf-cutting is not exempt. Turf-cutting may possibly be good agricultural practice according to modern notions of grassland management, but whoever seeks to establish this will have to get over the difficulty of *Meriden and Solihull A.C. v. Tyacke,* 1950, in which the following passage of the judgment makes the difficulties clear: " The respondent, who seems to be an unorthodox farmer (if that is a correct description of him), in order to rid one of his fields of parasites with which he found it infested . . . decided to cut and remove the turf and resow the field. He sold the turf for £80 an acre to a contractor who was to come in and buy the turf and take it away. The contractor did not work very fast, but eventually he did come and take away some of the turf as he felt disposed, and the respondent re-sowed it. In the meantime the full-grown cattle were allowed to come on to the land and feed on such of the turf as had not been taken away, because apparently the parasites were of a curious nature and only attacked the young and not the full-grown cows. How it can be said in those circumstances that the respondent was using land as meadow and pasture ground only, it is difficult to understand. That he is using it as pasture one would concede, but he is not using it as pasture ground only; he is using it partly as pasture and partly as a source of supply of the turf which he has sold to somebody else."

There are numerous instances where land has been held to be rateable in similar circumstances; notably land used for tipping spoil and land used as a caravan site.

Agricultural buildings

The definition of " agricultural buildings " bristles with difficulties. Section 2 (2) defines them as " buildings (other than dwelling-houses) occupied together with agricultural land . . . or being or forming part of a market garden and used solely in connection with agricultural operations thereon ". It will be seen that in order to satisfy the definition there must be two distinct elements:

    (i) the buildings must be occupied together with agricultural land; and

    (ii) they must be used solely in connection with agricultural operations on the land.

The first obvious conclusion to be drawn from this is that there must be some agricultural land occupied together with any given building before the building can qualify for agricultural relief. For example, a disused cotton mill surrounded by concrete converted for housing poultry on the deep litter system would presumably be rateable. There is, however, a second and more difficult limitation which follows from the use of the word "thereon". It would appear that the land upon which the agricultural operations take place and the buildings must both be in the occupation of the same person.

An excellent illustration of this principle arose in *Perrins v. Draper*, 1953. This was a Lands Tribunal decision, later affirmed in the Court of Appeal. In that case a dairy building where milk was cooled, bottled and pasteurised was used partly for milk from the farm of which the dairy building formed part and partly for milk from a neighbouring farm occupied by the appellant's brother. It was held that in these circumstances the building could not be described as a building used solely in connection with agricultural operations on the land *together with which it was occupied*, and that the building would accordingly be rateable.

Intensive livestock production

The difficulties inherent in the definition laid down in the 1928 Act have been highlighted by the increasing use in recent years of intensive methods of livestock rearing. The widespread use of broiler houses, deep-litter houses and Danish piggeries have raised some tricky rating problems, which depend almost entirely upon whether land in the same occupation is being used in connection with the buildings.

Fortunately it has been held that the extent to which the land is used, as compared with the use which is made of the buildings, is strictly irrelevant and need not be considered. In *Thompson v. Milk Marketing Board*, 1952, the Court of Appeal reserved a decision of the Lands Tribunal where the tribunal had taken into account the extent to which use had been made of the surrounding land. The case concerned one of the Board's artificial insemination centres, where bulls were kept for the collection and distribution of what was described with remarkable delicacy as "a very important raw material for use in the agricultural industry". The bulls were housed mainly in buildings, but there were 29 acres of land used for exercising and tethering them, also for producing some 20 to 25 per cent of their feed. The Court of Appeal held (i) that the extent to which the land was used in comparison with the use made of the buildings was not material, and (ii) that operations in the buildings might be quite different in character from those on the land.

Poultry houses

In view of the lack of direct High Court authority upon the question of broiler and other intensive poultry houses, it is inevitable that any suggestions we make must contain an element of speculation. But it seems to us that there are at least three ways

in which the occupier of a poultry farm may show that the buildings are "used solely in connection with agricultural operations
on the land together with which they are occupied". These appear
to be:

(a) He may be able to show that the birds have direct access
to the land. If such access is relied upon it should be of
provable agricultural value, and more than merely occasional.

(b) He may be able to show that the droppings have been used
as manure in the course of agricultural operations on the
land.

(c) He may be able to show that the rations have included a
certain proportion of home-grown feedingstuffs.

In cases where one or more of these three elements appear, we
would anticipate a good chance of successfully objecting to any
proposal that the buildings should be rated. No doubt there will
be numerous other examples of ways in which the use of a broiler
house can be, so to speak, integrated with the use of the surrounding land; but it does seem clear from such decisions of the courts
as exist that the buildings would be rateable unless there were
some such integration.

Piggeries

The intensive commercial piggery operated on the Danish model
raises similar difficulties. Here there is direct (but unfavourable)
High Court authority in *Pig Progeny Testing Board v. Greenall,*
1960. The appeal concerned the Board's testing station at Ham-
bleton in the West Riding of Yorkshire. The site consisted of some
nine acres, approximately an acre of which was taken up with
buildings accommodating some 400 little pigs. Approximately
a further acre was taken up with roads and yards, and the remaining seven acres were described as "a wilderness of weeds covered
with builders' rubble". It was intended that this land when
cleared should be used for the production of barley. The grain
from this would be used as feed, and the straw would provide
about a quarter of the straw required as bedding in the enterprise.
On these facts the Lands Tribunal had held that the buildings
were entitled to the benefit of agricultural relief. The Court of
Appeal, reversing this decision, held that the court must address
itself to the existing scheme of operations on the holding. It could
not take into account the future plans of the occupier, therefore
the hereditament must be restored to the valuation list. Though
it was said in argument that conditions were similar to those
operating in a commercial piggery, we do not think that the
decision of the Court of Appeal in the testing station case has
any general bearing upon such piggeries. It should be considered
rather as an illustration of the principle that the material date,
when the enterprise must be considered in relation to rating, is the
date of the rating officer's proposal.

Land used for isolation

Much has been made before the Local Valuation Courts of the argument that, in the case of intensive production units, direct use of the land is made (even though the livestock may have no access to it) as a barrier against disease, noise or other forms of interference with the health or comfort of the stock. The High Court does not appear to have pronounced upon this contention, but similar arguments were used in a Lands Tribunal appeal (*Hallam v. James,* 1958) which concerned a mink farm. The farm occupied a total area of just over three acres, and included a house with a garage and three mink-sheds, standing on an area of about one quarter of an acre, enclosed by a fence unclimbable by mink, should they escape from the cages. There was also a shed in which the animals' food was prepared and stored, and where the animals were skinned and the pelts were treated for sale. The mink-sheds which were approximately 90 ft. long by 12 ft. wide, were described as " merely roofed shelters with open sides in which the wire-netting cages are installed ". A very small, virtually negligible, quantity of the feed was home produced. In considering the " barrier " argument, the Chairman of the tribunal said: " Mink farming must be so conducted that the animals cannot be allowed free run, and in that respect it differs little from intensive pig farming and battery and deep litter poultry systems. In all these cases land is required, at least in populous areas, to isolate pens and buildings from surrounding properties and to eliminate trouble from offensive odours emanating therefrom. The land, however, is necessarily subservient to the operations carried on in the buildings, and I think it can fairly be said that these agricultural operations can only be conducted in the open country or, alternatively, in more populous districts when surrounded with sufficient land to provide reasonable isolation. The buildings and the land are essentially one entity devoted to the animal husbandry practised thereon, and it is immaterial in considering the part played by the land that its main, if not only, function is to provide the necessary isolation for the buildings." On this basis the buildings concerned were found to be agricultural buildings, therefore derateable.

Buildings used jointly

It will have been seen from the decision in *Perrins v. Draper* that rating difficulties arise immediately a farmer allows any building on his own holding to be used by a neighbouring farmer. This would be so presumably if, for instance, a farmer allowed his grain-drier to be used by neighbours, whether or not they made a money payment for the privilege. Similar difficulties occur where a number of farmers combine to provide storage, drying or processing equipment for the use of members of a group, which may or may not be an agricultural co-operative under the Industrial and Provident Societies Acts.

The Rating and Valuation Act, 1961, makes the following provisions as to jointly used buildings (Fourth Schedule, paragraph 2):

(1) A building shall be treated as an agricultural building for the purposes of the Rating and Valuation (Apportionment) Act, 1928, if it is used solely in connection with agricultural operations carried on on agricultural land and is occupied either—

(a) by the occupiers of all that land, or

(b) by individuals who are appointed by the said occupiers for the time being to manage the use of the building and of whom each is an occupier of some of the land or a member of the board of directors or other governing body of such an occupier, being a body corporate:

Provided that this sub-paragraph shall not have effect if the number of the occupiers of all the said land exceeds 24, two or more persons occupying jointly being counted as one (but as a separate person from any of them who are occupying any of the land severally).

(2) Land occupied with a building as respects which the foregoing sub-paragraph has effect and used solely in connection with the use of the building shall be treated as agricultural land for the purposes of the said Act of 1928.

This provision clearly extends the relief granted under the 1928 Act to land and buildings occupied by or on behalf of a group of occupiers of agricultural land. To this there are substantially two provisos:

(a) that the total number of such occupiers must not exceed 24 (counting partnerships as one); and

(b) if the management of the building is delegated to some kind of management committee, then each member of the management committee must also be a member of the larger group.

We do not think that compliance with these conditions would involve any special difficulty for existing machinery groups.

Farmers' garages

Where a farm building is used partly as an implements shed and partly as a garage for the farmer's car, the question of rating again arises. There may be cases where the car is used solely in connection with the farmer's business, but it has been held that if a car is used both privately and for business the building in which it is garaged is not an agricultural building within the meaning of section 2, consequently it will be rateable.

Farm houses and farm cottages

We have already seen that the gross value for rating purposes is ascertained by reference to the rent at which a property might be expected to be let on the open market, subject to certain assumptions about repairs. The process of assessment is similar with agricultural dwelling-houses, but the Local Government Act, 1929, lays down that the valuation must be made on the basis that the house is tied to its agricultural use. Section 72 provides that "the gross value for rating purposes of a house occupied in connection with agricultural land and used as the dwelling-house of a person who—

(a) is primarily engaged in carrying on or directing agricultural operations on that land; or

(b) is employed in agricultural operations on that land in the service of the occupier thereof and is entitled, whether as tenant or otherwise, so to use the house only while so employed,

shall, so long as the house is so occupied and used, be estimated by reference to the rent at which the house might reasonably be expected to let from year to year *if it could not be occupied and used otherwise than as aforesaid*".

This section therefore gives an indirect form of relief to farm houses and cottages. It does not automatically follow that the gross value of an agricultural dwelling-house must necessarily be less than that of a similar house used as a residence and in no way tied to farming. It merely restricts the hypothetical, or notional, tenancy, which is the basic assumption for estimating value to the agricultural community; and by so limiting the assumed demand it tends to reduce rental value. The practical effects of this form of relief are consequently of greater value in areas of high amenity and high rateable values. In what may be called the "deep rural" areas, where rateable values generally may be expected to be low, the section is of smaller practical importance.

A good deal of case law has accumulated upon the precise scope of section 72, particularly in relation to farm houses. It will be noted that, in the words of the section, the person occupying the dwelling-house must (in the case of a farm house) be *primarily engaged* in agricultural work on the land with which the house is occupied. This is hardly the place for an evaluation of such expressions as " gentleman farmer, hobby farmer, part-time farmer or twilight farmer "; but it has been held, for example, in *Gammans v. Parsons* (Lands Tribunal), 1953, that a farm house occupied by a solicitor carrying on a busy practice would not qualify for the rating relief afforded by that section.

Sporting rights

In many cases the sporting rights over a farm are liable to be charged to local rates. The question of whether or no is so studded with ifs and buts that it defies simplification. The position is best illustrated by listing the most likely circumstances in which sporting rights are liable to be exercised, and noting to what extent rating applies. In each instance we start with the landowner, be he lord of a million acres or a family farmer.

Case 1. The owner occupies the farm and exercises the sporting rights himself. The sporting rights are not rateable.

Case 2. The owner occupies the farm and lets the sporting rights by deed. Rateable: either the owner or the sporting tenant may be rated.

The deciding factor here is the letting by deed. A deed is a more elaborate document than a mere " agreement " as an instrument for transferring property rights or interests from one person to another. It must be sealed—none of your sixpenny stamps. In some transactions a deed is compulsory. One of them is the letting of sporting rights to a third party who has no other legal interest in the land, e.g., when a landowner lets the shooting over his tenanted farms to a city stockbroker. But a person may acquire the rights by simpler methods. In that case they are, legally, not " let "; the sportsman merely has a licence to exercise them. Letting or licence, it makes no difference to the day's bag, but the distinction is important as it affects the rating position.

Case 3. The owner occupies the farm and lets the sporting rights, though not by deed. Not rateable.

Case 4. The owner lets the farm but reserves the sporting rights for his own use. Rateable: the owner is liable for payment.

Case 5. The owner lets the farm, reserves the sporting rights, and lets them by deed. Rateable: either the owner or the sporting tenant may be rated.

Case 6. The owner lets the farm, reserves the sporting rights, and lets them but not by deed. Rateable: the owner is liable for the rates.

Case 7. The owner lets the farm with sporting rights included; the tenant exercises them himself. Not rateable.

Case 8. The owner lets the farm with sporting rights included; the tenant sublets them by deed. Rateable: either the tenant or the sporting tenant is liable.

Case 9. The owner lets the farm with sporting rights included; the tenant sublets them but not by deed. Not rateable.

Case 10. The owner lets the farm with sporting rights included; the tenant sublets the farm and retains them for his own amusement. Rateable: the original tenant is liable.

Chapter 38

INCOME TAX

Among the many impositions which draw the farmer into the common fold of taxpayers, Income Tax is the largest drain on his resources. It is levied afresh every year, at a varying so-much-in-the-pound, on his *income*—and while that may seem self-evident, the word needs some emphasis to distinguish it from capital.

Income Tax is the largest drain on his resources.

Income arises from so many sources—from the weekly wage packet to the ownership of a thousand ships—that there can be no single formula by which the " taxable " income from one and all can be calculated. In consequence the experts have devised five pigeonholes into one of which every source of income must come to roost. They are known as Schedules, and each has its own formula.

Schedule A applies to the ownership of landed property (farms, houses, flats, factories, forests, etc.)

Schedule B applies to the occupation of certain kinds of land.

Schedule C applies to dividends from certain investments.

Schedule D applies to the profits from any trade, profession or vocation—and that includes farming.

Schedule E applies to wages, salaries and pensions.

Before we consider the rules applying to each schedule, one point should be made clear. No matter under what schedule it is calculated, income tax is still the same income tax. That is to say, a farmer may own and occupy a farm, hold a block of shares in Finer Fertilisers, Ltd., and earn a salary for part-time work in the local slaughterhouse. For each of these sources of income a separate assessment will be made, but the total amount of tax he pays will be based on the sum of all the parts.

The rate at which tax is charged and the allowances which may be claimed are made official each year in the Finance Act, and given wide publicity by the press and H.M. Inspectors of Taxes. Since they become so soon out of date, it is not proposed to include this year's rates in this chapter, which otherwise deals with less changeable legislation. Furthermore, since the Income Tax Act, 1952—the " parent " of present-day tax law—runs to 532 sections and 24 schedules, the following can be but a narrow outline of the subject as affecting the farmer.

Schedule A

Tax under Schedule A, which is sometimes called the " Landlord's Property Tax ", is charged on the *ownership* of landed property, whether it is let to someone else or occupied by the owner. This part of the chapter is therefore of no practical value to tenant-farmers.

The basis of assessment is the Annual Value, and under section 82 of the Income Tax Act this means:

(i) the annual rent of the property, if it is let at a rack rent (namely, its full annual value, or near it, assuming the tenant pays the usual tenant's rates and taxes and the landlord bears the usual landlord's charges, including repairs and insurance) fixed by agreement within the past seven years; or

(ii) if the property is not so let, the rack rent at which it is worth to be let by the year.

Where a farm is in fact let on about the best possible terms, the annual value presents no difficulty. But where it is owner-occupied the problem becomes more theoretical.

It was for a long time the practice for Schedule A valuations to be made every five years, but the war put an end to the cycle and the 1952 Act provides for revaluations to be started again when Parliament wills it. Because of this long hold-up very many farms are assessed at a figure far below the rent they would bring in if relet in the open market: a state of affairs that gives rise to no complaints.

The annual value is not the figure on which tax is levied, for a number of deductions may first be made from it. They are:

(i) Any land tax payable on the property (see page 276).

(ii) Public rates payable for drainage, fencing or embanking (see page 157).

(iii) The average sum spent by the owner during the past 21 years on sea-walls or other defences against the sea or tidal rivers.

(iv) Five-sixths of any tithe redemption annuity (see page 273).

(v) Repairs allowance. This is at standard rates, depending on the nature and annual value of the property in question. It may be claimed even if nothing in fact has been spent on repairs.

In the case of an owner-occupied farm, the statutory repairs allowance may be summarised thus:

(a) For the farm land and the buildings, deduct one-eighth of their full annual value.

(b) Houses and cottages.

A.V. not exceeding £40	— deduct one-fourth
£40–£50	— deduct £10
£50–£100	— deduct one-fifth
A.V. exceeding £100	— deduct £20 plus one-sixth of the A.V. over £100

Where a farm is let and the owner does all repairs, he may claim the same repairs allowances; but the farmhouse is included with the land and buildings, so that it enjoys only the one-eighth allowance.

Here follows an example to illustrate how these rules operate.

Farmer A owns and occupies Excise Farm. Its gross annual value for Schedule A is £520, which includes the farmhouse assessed at £60, five workmen's cottages assessed at £12 each and a dower house assessed at £112. Land tax amounts to £30 a year, and there is a tithe redemption annuity of £18. He pays an owner's drainage rate of £8.

Annual value ...		£520
Deduct: Land tax ...	£30	
T.R.A. $\frac{5}{6}$ or £18 ...	15	
Drainage rate ...	8	
Repairs allowance:		
Farmhouse $\frac{1}{8}$ × £60 ...	£12	
Dower house £20 + $\frac{1}{6}$ × £12 ...	22	
Cottages $\frac{1}{4}$ × £60 ...	15	
Land and buildings $\frac{1}{8}$ × £288 ...	36	138
Net assessment		£382

The figure of £382 is that on which Income Tax is due from the owner. In practice, the demand for tax is served on the occupier, but if he is merely a tenant he settles the bill and is entitled to deduct the amount from his next payment of rent.

The Maintenance Claim

The statutory repairs allowance, we observed a while back, may be deducted from the gross Schedule A assessment whether or not the owner in fact spends a penny piece on keeping his property in shape. Very generous, the owner may concede: but supposing he spends more than his standard allowance? It is a pleasure to assure him that the tax laws continue in his favour, for he has a right to make what is called a Maintenance Claim in respect of the surplus expenditure. Section 101 of the Income Tax Act, 1952, expresses his right in these words:

" If the owner of any land (inclusive of farmhouses and other buildings, if any) or of any houses . . . shows that the cost to him of maintenance, repairs, insurance and management, according to the average of the preceding five years, has exceeded " the statutory repairs allowances, he shall be entitled " on making a claim for the purpose, to repayment of tax on the excess."

Several million explanatory words have been written on what items can be included as " repairs, insurance and management ", and it is hard to cover the subject in less. Yet there is one general rule of thumb. In deciding whether or not to include a particular expense in the detailed claim, ask yourself: " Was the expenditure necessary to maintain the existing rental value? " Repairs to the roof—yes. Repainting the woodwork—yes. Repapering the front parlour at a cost of £20—yes. Decorating the front parlour walls with damask at a cost of £250—no!

Again, " repairs " does not include—with the exception mentioned on page 271—improvements. To repair a dutch barn is one thing; to erect a new one is another. A test of eligibility, which of course can only be applied where a farm is let, is this: " Did the landlord obtain additional rent for the work he did? " If so, in most cases the expense cannot be included.

The Maintenance Claim is submitted on Form 99, of which every Inspector of Taxes holds a supply in stock. The rational procedure is to fill in the form at about the same time every year, but taxpayers to whom dilatoriness comes naturally may claim up to six years back.

It will be seen from the law's phraseology that the Maintenance Claim is based on a five-year average. To illustrate this, we will work out this year's claim for Farmer A of Excise Farm, whose Schedule A assessment we have already calculated.

His statutory repair allowance amounted to £85. His accounts for the year just ended show a total expenditure of £70 on repairs and fire insurance. The previous year he spent £35; the year before that—the year that the chimney breast collapsed—£260. Four years ago, as he sees from the file wherein he preserves copies of previous maintenance claims, he spent £80; the year before £75.

In the last five years, then, Farmer A has spent a total of £520 in repairs and insurance. (Management expenses are rare on small properties: they include such luxuries as agents' salaries, certain legal charges, stamp duties on tenancy agreements, etc.) His current five-year average is therefore £104. This actual figure is compared with the statutory allowance of £85. He can reclaim tax on the balance of £19.

Schedule B

At one time Schedule B netted a rich harvest, but it has gradually been whittled down in scope and could probably be abolished altogether without yielding the nation up to bankruptcy. It is charged on the privilege of *occupying* certain types of land: notably woodlands which are not otherwise assessed under Schedule D, and amenity lands not occupied for commercial purposes; parks, pleasure gardens, recreation grounds, deer forests, grouse moors and so on.

Where it does apply, Schedule B is levied in addition to Schedule A. The assessable value is one-third of the annual value for Schedule A.

Schedule C

Tax under Schedule C is outside the scope of farming, and affects only the farmer who happens also to be an investor in, for example, consols. It is assessed on the actual amount received from interest, dividends and annuities payable out of public revenue.

Schedule D

This is the net in which the Chancellor of the Exchequer traps a proportion of the farmer's profits. It is charged on the profits of the *preceding* year, which can prove irksome to the taxpayer who last year did extremely well and frittered it away, but this year barely covers his expenses.

The income tax year runs from the 6th of April to the 5th of April next, and for many reasons it is convenient to adopt this as the accounting year. But if a farmer customarily makes up his accounts to 25th March, say, or 31st December, the inspector of taxes will normally accept the fact. In such event your Lady Day farmer will be taxed under Schedule D for the year 1961–62 (ending 5th April, 1962) on the profits for the year ending 25th March, 1961, and so on.

Farm accounts are a headache inseparable from agriculture, but they need not be elaborate for taxation purposes. The standard form familiar to the farmer is that supplied by the tax folk: Form 79D.

It breaks down into three parts: a valuation of live and dead stock and tillages, an account of cash paid out and received during the year, and a page of allowances for machinery and plant.

The Valuation

In assessing the profit (or loss) from a business, it is not sufficient to say, " I sold goods to a total of £3,000 and paid out £2,000 in stock and wages; therefore my income was £1,000 ". One must also take into account " paper " profits or losses, to do which one needs to take stock at the end of each year and compare the valuation with its equivalent of twelve months ago. Half of our exemplary trader's £2,000 may have been spent on goods which he still holds. Being potentially saleable, they are treated as an asset.

The valuation page of the farmer's income tax form gives a pretty complete list of live and dead assets: cattle, horses, sheep, pigs, crops, cereals, feedingstuffs, etc., each with a space for its number and value at the beginning and at the end of the year.

The Inspector of Taxes will consider any reasonable basis of valuation the farmer adopts, but prefers some orthodox method as one of the following.

Livestock are most commonly valued in one of two ways. On the " trading stock basis " the valuation is the total cost of the livestock or their total market value, whichever is the lower. In the case of beasts or birds bred on the farm, if their " cost " cannot otherwise be worked out, it may be estimated at 75 per cent of the value of each animal at the date of the valuation.

The " herd basis " is of more limited application. It applies only to " production herds ", such as dairy herds and ewe flocks kept for the sale of milk, wool, young animals or other produce. In other words, it is their *produce* from the sale of which the farmer makes or loses money. In this important respect they are distinguished from herds or flocks of beasts or poultry which are themselves reared for sale, such as fattening bullocks, flying flocks of ewes, or broiler chickens.

When the herd basis was first invented every farmer with a production herd was given a chance to opt for it within a specified time. Today it is normally given only to those newly started in farming. And they must make their choice not later than two years after the end of the first year of assessment for which they became chargeable under Schedule D in respect of farming profits, the first year of assessment being the year in which they took up farming. For example, if a new farmer starts a dairy herd during any part of the tax year ending 5th April, 1962, and wishes it to come under the herd basis, he must make written application to his Inspector of Taxes not later than 5th April, 1964. Such a choice must apply to all production herds of the same class. That is to say, a farmer with two dairy herds, one Friesian, one Ayrshire, must include both, not one or the other. For herds of different classes, however, separate elections are made. A farmer with a dairy herd and a ewe flock may choose to have one herd-based and leave the other alone so that it is treated as trading stock.

Having once chosen the herd basis it applies for as long as the farmer continues to keep production herds of that class. There is no right to chop and change between that and the trading stock basis according to how the trade winds blow.

The essence of the herd basis is that the value of the production animals is not brought into the valuations at the beginning and end of the year. They are regarded as a sort of capital investment whose interest, from the tax angle, lies in the income they produce: the milk, wool, lambs, eggs, etc.

The general effect of omitting the animals from the accounts is that any profit on the sale of the herd or flock or a substantial part of it—which means in effect more than 20 per cent—is not taxable. Correspondingly, if sold at a loss no relief can be claimed. But if up to about one-fifth of the herd, or individual animals, are sold without being replaced, then the profit or loss is taken into account. Finally, if additional beasts are brought in to increase the size of the herd or flock, the farmer cannot include the cost as an item of " cash paid out ".

We stated above that the right to apply for the herd basis is " normally " given only to those starting to farm for the first time. An exception is made where the whole or a substantial part of a production herd is compulsorily slaughtered, e.g., for reasons of foot-and-mouth or otherwise under the law relating to notifiable diseases. In such event the farmer receives compensation, and under the trading stock basis the amount would appear in his accounts as a receipt, so increasing his taxable profits. To spare him this additional distress, he may mitigate the tragedy by making a late election to the herd basis whereby the compensation money is, taxably speaking, forgotten.

Farm produce in hand—stacks of corn and hay, silage, roots, manures, feedingstuffs, fuel and so on—are measured and priced at their present day value on the farm.

Tillages, unexhausted manures and growing crops may be valued in detail as for a tenant-right valuation. But where their normal value does not exceed £700, the Inspector of Taxes will accept a signed statement—assuming of course, that it is true!—that their valuations at the beginning and end of the year did not materially differ. In that case no detailed valuation need be recorded.

Farm machinery is generally dealt with under a wear-and-tear system. This is calculated by taking last year's valuation and deducting a standard percentage, depending on the nature of the plant or machinery, namely:

	Per cent
(a) Steam boilers, engines, portable steam engines, threshing machines (other than peg drum) and fixed plant ...	5
(b) Electric installations	7½
(c) Petrol or oil-driven tractors	22½
(d) Binders, reapers and combine harvesters	15
(e) Sugar beet and potato harvesters and diggers	20
(f) Sprayers and flax-pulling machines	25
(g) Commercial motor vehicles (steam)	15
(h) „ „ „ (internal combustion) ...	20
(i) Motor-cars (the allowance is restricted if the car is also used for purposes other than farming)	20
(j) All other types of farm machinery and implements, including peg drum threshing machines, portable poultry (and similar) sheds and incubators	10

For some years past the wear-and-tear allowance has been, and currently remains, five-fourths, or one-and-a-quarter times the above rates.

In addition to these annual allowances, a farmer may claim capital allowances for plant and machinery bought at any time during the past accounting year. New plant and machinery attracts an investment allowance of 20 per cent, plus an initial allowance of 10 per cent. For second-hand stuff, and motors whether new or second-hand, an initial allowance of 30 per cent may be claimed. These benefits sound much the same, since both add up to 30 per cent; in fact they work rather differently in practice of accounting.

Where the farm shows a loss

" All this talk about profits ", objects the reader who last year lost all his crops through coastal flooding, his cattle through foot-and-mouth and his staff to the new town: " What about the farmer who makes a loss? "

If the farmer can prove that he has sustained a loss in any year of assessment, he may set it off against his total income for that year and claim repayment of tax in consequence. Supposing, however, that his income comes solely from farming, and that he has too few or no stocks and shares, part-time jobs, P.O. savings, caravan rents, or other wolf-scarers to call upon? The answer then is that—subject to rules which need not be expounded here—it is carried forward year by year, and set against next and the next and the next year's profits, until finally it is wholly repaid or, if he continues to make losses, the farmer goes bankrupt or turns to a more profitable line of living.

Schedule E

This concerns every farmer who employs workers, for it is the schedule under which income tax is charged on salaries, wages and pensions.

It is put into practice through Pay As You Earn, a system whose workings, omitting complications, may be summed up in tolerably few words. Every taxpayer, rich or poor, has to fill in each year a form showing his income from all sources for the year ending 5th April. On the same form he claims for various allowances: personal allowance, children, dependent relatives, life assurance, and so on. From the information returned the Inland Revenue folk calculate the tax payable by the individual and accordingly give him a Code Number, on a form which shows the details used to calculate that number.

Since the code number depends on allowances, it follows that two people in similar jobs, earning the same wages, may yet have different numbers. George and Jim, the two pigmen, both work for the same screw, but George, being a bachelor and entitled to fewer tax allowances, will be coded higher than Jim with his wife and six children.

The employer is notified of the code number applicable to each of his employees, and he works these in conjunction with a volume of Tax Tables supplied by the Inland Revenue. There are two sets of tables for every week in the income tax year, or monthly tables for those who are paid once a month. Table A shows the " free pay " in relation to a long column of code numbers—in other words, the tax allowance as they accumulate weekly or monthly. The employer deducts this accumulated free pay from the total wages or salary paid to his employee since the tax year began. What remains is the " taxable pay " received by the employee to date.

Turning to Table B he finds how much tax is due on this taxable pay. He deducts the appropriate amount, and the balance goes into the wage packet.

As a further duty to the Inland Revenue the employer—who is of course responsible for paying the Collector of Taxes the income tax due from his workers—keeps a set of tax deduction cards, on which he records each employee's total pay and total tax deducted. At the end of the tax year he submits them to the Collector with an accompanying " Employer's Annual Return ".

CAPITAL EXPENDITURE ALLOWANCES

In our outline of Schedule A, the landlord's property tax, we showed that an owner is given a tax-free allowance for repairs to his property, based on a standard scale. If he spends more than the " statutory " allowance on repairs, insurance and management he may reclaim tax on the excess by means of a maintenance claim. In general, he cannot include in his claim the cost of any items of an *improving* nature.

It is now our privilege to introduce section 314 of the Income Tax Act, 1952, by which tax relief may be claimed on improvements, whether done by landlords or by tenants.

Where the owner or tenant of a farm incurs expenditure on the construction or improvement of farmhouses, farm buildings, cottages, fences or other works necessary for the proper working of the land, he can claim one-tenth of the cost as an allowance for income tax purposes in each of the ten years following the year in which he made the expenditure. In ten years time, therefore, he will have reclaimed income tax on the whole amount.

The " other works " referred to include such improvements as drainage and sewerage, supplies of electricity or water, planting shelter belts, reclamation of waste land, and so forth. Where the expenditure is on the farmhouse, only one-third of the cost can be claimed. Indeed, if the accommodation and amenities of the house are " out of due relation to the nature of the farm "—as where from a stately and historic home you manage ten acres of poultry and pig land—the allowance may be even less.

A claim must be for *capital* expenditure, not for the sort of running repair that may be included in the maintenance claim. It is made on a special form, No. 461, " Income Tax: Claim for Allowance for Capital Expenditure on Agricultural or Forestry Buildings and Works ". The relief comes to the farmer primarily by being treated as a set-off against his " agricultural income ", that is to say, his Schedule A assessment (if he owns his farm) or his Schedule D income from farming the land. If the allowance exceeds his agricultural income in any year, he may carry forward the unsatisfied balance until times and his profits improve.

Where a farm tenant who is in course of enjoying his ten-year relief quits before the last instalment is exhausted, similarly where an owner sells the farm, the new tenant or owner takes over the privilege of claiming relief. But if on a change of tenancy an incoming tenant does not pay the outgoer for capital improvements made by him, the future allowances pass to the landlord.

Investment Allowances

In addition to the 10-instalment capital expenditure claim, as a further encouragement to spend money on improving farm land, a once-and-for-all *investment allowance* can be claimed on all improvements eligible for the capital expenditure claim. This is at the rate of 10 per cent. The combined effect is that the improving farm landlord or tenant who spends, for example, £1,000 net (i.e., after deducting any government grants) on a new approved implement shed, may reclaim tax on £200 for the first year and £100 for each of the next nine years, making 110 per cent in all.

As a final return to the maintenance claim, we hinted that while as a general rule only repairs, not improvements, may be included, there are a few exceptions. Typically they arise where, for instance, a landlord is compelled to improve his dairy buildings to comply with the Milk and Dairies Regulations. Such " capital " expenditure, to the extent that it is made on new assets, is not only admissible in the maintenance claim but may also attract the 10 per cent investment allowance. In these cases, the combined 110 per cent relief is charged against tax over five years: 30 per cent in the first, and 20 per cent in each of the four succeeding.

And as a final return to the capital expenditure claim, many over-optimistic farmers and their jealous foes seem to think that the *whole* of their capital outlay on improvements is repaid by a philanthropic treasury. May we point out that only the *tax* on the expenditure finds its way back to their pockets or their credit accounts.

Chapter 39

TITHE AND LAND TAX

TITHE REDEMPTION ANNUITY

Tithe is one of the oldest tributes arising out of the land. This fact will in no way reconcile the tithe-payer who, conforming to other religions or none, resents making contributions to the established church. A short review of its history will, however, help to explain how and why many farms are saddled with Tithe Redemption Annuities.

Of all the taxes and charges inflicted on farmers, tithe is the only one whose origin cannot be dated. All we know about the first tithe-payer is that he yielded one-tenth (tithe means tenth) of his produce to the parish priest, and in time this originally voluntary contribution became a legal obligation.

Yielded one-tenth of his produce.

In Norman times most land was subject to tithe, a distinction being made between predial tithe, a tenth part of the crops that the land produced, and mixed tithe, a tenth of the produce of creatures that lived off the land, such as milk, wool or butter. The creation of new tithes became one way of keeping up with

the Fitzjoneses, in connection with William the Conqueror's practice of rewarding his followers with presents of other folks' lands.
The new lords of the manor would build or improve a church,
endow it with tithe, and reserve to themselves and their heirs the
advowson, which gave them the right to appoint the rector. The
stipend of the rector (i.e., ruler or governor) was known as rectorial
tithe.

By a long drawn out process of takeover bids, many advowsons
were accumulated by monasteries, which appointed themselves
rectors of the manorial churches and diverted the attaching rectorial
tithes to their own coffers. To discharge the parochial church
duties they appointed a clerk to act as their vicar (i.e., deputy or
substitute). Where in this manner tithe became severed from the
original benefice and attached to a monastery or other ecclesiastical
body, it was called a propriation.

Whereas a vicar was usually dependent for his living upon the
" corporate " rector, the vicarage—meaning the office he held—
might be endowed with tithes of its own. So to rectorial tithes
and propriations of tithes there were added vicarial tithes.

Collectively these three were all forms of ecclesiastical tithes.
When Henry VIII dissolved the monasteries he became possessed
not only of a rich harvest of land and buildings but the right to
receive tithes attached to them. Numbers of these rights he sold
for a capital sum to persons having no connection with the church.
These became lay tithes, or tithes impropriate.

During most of their history tithes were paid in kind, the local
farmers sharing the burden of filling the great tithe barn. But in
many parishes it became the accepted practice to compound for
their tithes by the payment of money based on the value of the
produce due from them. In 1836 the Tithe Act compulsorily did
away with tithe in kind, and substituted Tithe Rentcharge. The
annual amount fluctuated with farming prosperity, and was calculated on a local basis. In each parish surveyors assessed the
average annual value of the tithes paid in kind over the last seven
years. This sum was apportioned among all the lands in the parish
according to their productive capacity. The figure allotted to any
one field or farm was called the commuted amount, and used as
the basis for future calculations to vary with the current average
market prices of wheat, barley and oats.

The 1836 system was maintained until 1918, when the rocketing
prices of corn in the first world war raised the burden of tithe to
unheard of heights, and new legislation imposed a brake on it.
The Tithe Act, 1918, pegged the annual value at a fixed amount
for a specific period, at the end of which the Tithe Act, 1925,
prolonged the process.

The 1925 Act also provided for the payment of a sinking fund, to be set aside out of the receipts from the tithe redemption payers and allowed to accumulate at compound interest for 85 years, after which there would be no more payments demanded. Since farming was still prospering, it seemed a tolerable arrangement.

However, not many years after 1925, depression took over the plough, and not a few farmers rebelled at the imposition of tithe rentcharge. By 1934, it had become necessary to refer the whole subject to a Royal Commission, whose recommendations were largely made law by the Tithe Act of 1936. Even as tithe in kind had lost its identity in tithe rentcharge, so was tithe rentcharge transformed into today's Tithe Redemption Annuities. Under the Act the owners of tithe rentcharge were given an issue of 3 per cent redemption stock, backed by the State and redeemable in 60 years. Rentcharge payers in future would be charged with annuities to provide the interest on the stock as well as a sinking fund for its redemption.*

Calculation of T.R.A.

As related above, in 1836 a grand survey was undertaken of all tithe-paying parishes. The average annual value of the tithe paid in kind was translated into cash and apportioned over the lands concerned. Park Farm, for example, was saddled with a " commuted " amount of £100, Manor Farm with £66 6s. 8d., Chilly Comfort with £10 a year. Subject to alterations which might have occurred in a hundred years owing to changes in the farm boundaries, those 1836 values were used as a yardstick in calculating tithe redemption annuities in 1936. If any of the land chargeable to tithe rentcharge was agricultural land on 1st April, 1936, the amount of the annuity was fixed at £91 11s. 2d. per £100 commuted value; but if none of the land was agricultural, the rate was £105 per cent.

Park Farm, therefore, now pays a redemption annuity of £91 11s. 2d. a year; Manor Farm £61; while the owner of Chilly Comfort, which became a holiday camp in 1934, receives a demand for 10 guineas a year.

Payment of T.R.A.

Tithe Redemption Annuities are payable once a year, in arrear, on 1st October, and are destined to come to an end in 1996. They are payable by the *owner* of the land which gave them birth. " Owner " normally means what it says, but where a farm is let

---

* In practice one-sixth of the receipts from tithe redemption annuities are set aside as a sinking fund; the remainder may be regarded as spending money. The sinking fund is in the nature of capital money. This explains why, in calculating an owner's assessment to property tax, only five-sixths of the T.R.A. may be deducted from gross value. See page 263.

on lease for more than 14 years at less than two-thirds of its full net annual value as calculated for income tax, the lessee is included in the term. Grange Farm, for instance, has a net annual value for Schedule A income tax of £150. It was let two years ago to Farmer Fortunate on a 21-year lease at £75 a year. Farmer Fortunate is therefore liable to pay the T.R.A. of £6 a year. Had it been let for £100 or more, the landlord would have been liable.

LAND TAX

This imposition, like tithe, is of considerable antiquity: indeed it may be regarded as a descendant of the tenth-century Danegeld, a form of blackmail directed towards pacifying the Danish invaders. As we know it today, however, Land Tax was first imposed in 1692 as a means of paying for yet another of our wars with France. It persisted long after the last shot was fired, at a varying rate in the pound every year, until the Land Tax Act, 1797, equipped it with stabilisers. The Act decreed that thereafter England and Wales should yield up as land tax a fixed sum of some £2 million a year. That sum was portioned out among the parishes in the form of annual quotas, and those parochial quotas remain the basis on which the tax has been charged to this day.

The quotas are collected by levying the tax at the rate of not less than one penny but not more than one shilling in the pound on the annual value of all landed properties, apart from some which are exempt or those on which it has been redeemed. In view of the fact that property values in any parish would alter from time to time, one going up while another went down, the tax would be liable to vary on any one property. But from 1949 onwards it was generally stabilised. Since then each property is charged every year with the land tax it rendered for the " basic " year 1948–49.

The land tax year runs from 25th March, and the tax is payable in one sum on 1st January intervening. As a rule the Inspector of Taxes sends a demand for it at the same time as his demand for Schedule A income tax. It is collected from the occupier. If he is a tenant he may deduct it from his next payment of rent to his landlord; but he may expressly agree with his landlord to bear the burden of it himself.

For the indigent landowner there are special dispensations. If his total income from all sources, as estimated for income tax purposes, does not exceed £160 a year, he may claim total exemption from land tax. Where it lies between £160 and £400 he may claim relief from half of it.

Redemption of Land Tax

A land tax payer who wishes to be quit of it can do so by making a once-for-all payment of 25 times the annual charge. This is known as voluntary redemption.

Since 1st April, 1951, it has been made compulsory to redeem land tax the next time a property changes hands, either by sale or on inheritance or on the grant of a lease for 21 years or more. The responsibility for compulsory redemption is as follows:

(i) If the property is sold or given away, the purchaser or receiver must redeem the tax.

(ii) If it is leased for 21 years or more, the owner redeems.

(iii) If the owner dies, in the ordinary way the personal representatives of the deceased must see to its redemption.

In all cases the person liable to pay the redemption money must notify the Inland Revenue authorities. As with voluntary redemption, the cost is 25 times the annual charge. Once the tax has been redeemed it ceases ever to be payable again as from the last quarter-day before the date on which the redemption money became due.